The PenDelfin
Collectors Handbook

Stella M Ashbrook

Frank Salmon

Francis Joseph
London
1 870703-62-6

Acknowledgements

Having produced numberous notes and scribbles over the years about PenDelfin, I can honestly say that without the support of my friends and family it would never have reached the stage of a complete handbook. Their support and encouragement over the past nine months in particular has been one hundred percent, and I thank them sincerely.

My warmest thanks are due to Francis Salmon my publisher for his continual faith and endless reassurance, and to Robert Prescott-Walker for his editorial experience and his unreserved time.

I would like to thank PenDelfin for their help, in particular Pauline and Arthur Morley and Ann Carney for her guidence with all the enquiries that I threw her way.

The Collectors of PenDelfin have been wonderful. Sincere thanks to David Spindley, Mr and Mrs Elliot and Mrs J Swann for the use of their collections which formed the basis of the pictures in this book. Also a huge thank you to Mr and Mrs A Buchan for the numerous cups of tea and cake while gathering snippets of information whilst perusing their collection and to Mrs J Eckersley for her thoughts and ideas which were an inspiration.

I have had a great deal of enjoyment and satisfaction from researching and compiling this guide. Having a full time job, a home to run and my husband Robert, time was so precious my other half learned to ring before coming home to check if we needed a takeaway meal. We often did, and without his full support this book could not have been completed.

© 1997 Francis Joseph Publications

Published in the UK by
Francis Joseph Publications
15 St Swithuns Road
London SE13 6RW
Telephone: 0181 318 9580

Production: Francis Salmon
Photography: Trevor Leak

Typeset by E J Folkard Computer Services
199 Station Road, Crayford, Kent DA1 3QF

Printed in Great Britain by
The Greenwich Press, London SE7

ISBN 1-870703-62-6

All the information and valuations have been compiled from reliable sources and every effort has been made to eliminate errors and questionable data. Nevertheless the possibility of error always exists. The publisher and author will not be held responsible for losses which may occur in the purchase, sale or other transaction of items because of information contained herein. Readers who feel they have discovered errors are invited to write and inform us so that these may be corrected in subsequent editions.

Francis Joseph is an independent publisher and is no way associated with PenDelfin.

Contents

Foreword 4

Introduction 6

PenDelfin and Why 8

Three Women, One Man and a Spirited Team 10

PenDelfin Variants 13

Repaints and Restorations 16

Colour Gallery 17

Variations of Colour and Decoration 65

Process and Progress 68

The Most Elusive Pieces 71

How to Identify PenDelfin 73

Backstamps and Labels 75

Listings and Price Guide 77

Recent Prices achieved at auction 102

Index 103

Foreword

Frank Salmon

Little did I know that when I left Burnley in 1977 that I would be embarking on a career as a London publisher. Having been in the business for over twelve years now, I was delighted at the prospect of coming back home and producing a collectors book about PenDelfin – the famous Burnley 'collectable'.

It seems that the original concept behind PenDelphin was the theme of myth and legend, focussing on local history and the Pendle Witches and the idea of producing rabbits was probably something of an afterthought. But what an afterthought it turned out to be! All new businesses struggle in their early years and for Jean and Jeannie this was no exception. When the idea of comical and cheeky rabbits was first mooted, they treated the project with the enthusiasm and hard work for which they have been rightly recognised. Hard work was no stranger to them but what they could not plan for was the amazing response from the public. They had managed to produce charming characters in real life situations that sparked a hint of affection and recognition in all who saw them. When Jean designed her first models she was not to know that she would capture the hearts of an international band of collectors.

We must however be wary of calling the first enthusiasts 'collectors'. In those early post-war years in industrial Lancashire, with rationing only very recently a thing of the past, there was simply no notion of 'collecting', especially in regard to a family of cheeky, playful rabbits! No, people bought PenDelfin because they liked them. They brought warmth and colour into the home. They were well made, carefully and expertly painted, and inexpensive. In today's age, collecting is all the rage, but in the 1950s, your product had to shout out to the passer-by in shops up and down the country, and sell on its own merits. PenDelfin consequently became the first stonecraft models to establish a niche in the giftware market, and today are hugely popular as collectable items too. When other producers have come and gone, it is undoubted that PenDelfin will continue to capture the hearts of the collector – as well as the passer-by who happens upon a chance meeting with one of these characters – and simply *has* to buy him.

My first association with PenDelfin goes back to 1958 when **Twins** was first introduced. My Auntie Lydia bought this piece for my mother, because she had just given birth to twins – of which I was one! Now thats funny, because in the book we record the date of introduction as 1962, but my mum swears it was a 1958 present and so, baffled, I can only say that my mum got hold of a very early piece or that

4

her recollections must be a bit hazy. However, it could be that I was born with my sister, Helen, in 1962, and by some freak accident everyone recorded the event as 1958. That makes us four years younger. Now that really appeals to me!

A special note of thanks must go to Pauline and Arthur Morley who gave up a whole day to our visit and treated us to lunch. They gave us a very interesting tour of Cameron Mill and showed us all the processes involved in making their PenDelfin range. Everyone was very friendly and full of tales and recollections about developments at PenDelfin over the

years. Stella is pictured with Arthur and Pauline above.

I would also like to thank Mr and Mrs Elliott from Rainham in Essex. They have a lovely collection of PenDelfin rabbits and they treated us to many cups of tea over a days shooting with my photographer, Trevor Leak.

Also of great assistance was David Spinney from Blackpool who entertained myself and Stephen Perry (photographer's assistant) whilst we photographed some very rare and interesting items.

Stephen Perry

Whilst at the Mill we also bumped into Mr Poyser who had just brought in a very rare Father (Dungarees). He was delighted to find this very valuable and, pursuing a career in photography, we encouraged him to take the photograph of Stella with Pauline and Arthur above.

Finally, a note of thanks to Eric Bernardes who has represented PenDelfin for many years and who first suggested the idea of this book to me. What a good idea!

Mr Poyser

Mr & Mrs Elliott

David Spinney

Introduction

Stella Ashbrook

Welcome to the first edition of the PenDelfin Collectors Handbook. This has become necessary to produce because PenDelfin is now officially a 'collectable', or 'collectible' as our American cousins would say. In fact, a good claim can be made for PenDelfin to be the first of all the modern collectables. Starting in the 1950s it must surely rank among the oldest of its closest competitors. However, interest is such that the very early models that are no longer in production are now highly sought after, as evidenced by recent auction prices and collector expenditure. This guide includes an invaluable listing, including secondary market prices that have been reached through auctions, collector trading, or through the PenDelfin Collectors Club. Obviously the rarer the figure or ornament, the higher the prices that have been reached. Collectors will find the guide useful for identifying models, their approximate dates of introduction and withdrawal and using the colour reference we give to see if theirs is different in any way. The more I researched, the more I became aware of the great diversity and range that PenDelfin has offered and still offers today.

Collecting is addictive and, once you have been bitten by the bug, enthusiasm takes over. Questions are asked like, 'When was this item produced?' and 'Can I still buy it today?', 'How much is it worth?' I hope this guide will provide the answer. The information contained within is as accurate and consistent as possible and with the combined knowledge of collectors, myself, and PenDelfin, a great deal of ground has been covered. Obviously, there will be some items out there that are very rare indeed and which are as yet unrecorded. If you find such an example, please let me know through writing to me care of the publishers address given at the front of this book.

The secondary market – i.e. auction houses, dealers, fairs etc., are becoming increasingly aware of the collectable market for PenDelfin, and so in turn they are helping to supply the items for which there is a lot of demand. Such activity will hopefully keep prices down, though there is so much recent interest from collectors that it is only to be expected that prices of early pieces will continue to increase in the forseeable future. It is even possible to contact collectors on the Internet! This is especially important for collectors in the USA, because the very early models were not exported there (in fact not until the 1960s) and keen US collectors are on the look out for those hard-to-find examples. If the experience of other collectables is anything to go by, enthusiasm for PenDelfin will be not only among the older pieces but also the exclusive designs, the yearly collectors club models and the limited editions. Watch this space!

PenDelfin is diverse enough to appeal to all and whether you have a collection of 100 pieces or just a handful, the thrill of collecting will compel you to search for the figure you want.

PenDelfin and Why

1953 was notable for two very important reasons. It was the year of the Coronation of Queen Elizabeth II, and it was also the year in which two young women, Jean Walmsley Heap and Jeannie Todd set up business in a garden shed. Little did they know then that they were to become doyens of their own art, much admired throughout the world. They started with models of witches, fairies, characters of myth and legend, and seemingly as an afterthought – rabbits.

It was the looming hill of Pendle which dominates the town of Burnley and smaller towns and villages around it that gave birth to the name of PenDelfin. Pendle Hill, shaped like a huge whale, is famous throughout the region for the trials of the Pendle witches over two hundred years ago, which led to some of the accused being hanged. The top being accessible by public footpath, it is difficult to find anyone in the locality who has not walked up it at some stage in their lives. Inspired by the folklore of the witches, the name of the company and the first sculpted items were deeply rooted in the history and landscape of the area. Whilst those initial ideas did not materialise, the name of PenDelfin, a mixture of Pendle and Elfin, was to become internationally famous.

Jean Walmsley Heap and Jeannie Todd were full of boundless enthusiasm and it is therefore not surprising that they were to hit on an idea that would transform their fortunes. They decided to model rabbits with decidedly human characteristics – a mother and father rabbit that dressed as we do, and children at play in all the most pre-posessing guises that make children the 'loveable' creatures that they are. The partnership hit on an idea that was without parallel – affordable ornaments that reflected with humour the antics of adults and children. It was an idea that was to run and run.

Father Rabbit was the very first. He stands 8 inches high and has very large ears and a big head in comparison to the models we see today. Wearing dungarees, his bottom is a lot fatter than usual and the facial details seem to be more defined. He also has a tendency to fall over. In the early days Jean and Jeannie will have been unfamiliar with the need to centre the 'gravity' of the object so that it does not topple over. **Mother Rabbit** was made as a companion piece and, as is to be expected of rabbits, the two were soon to become many many more . . . The success of the early models was to make the future of PenDelfin very secure and with drive and initiative the partnership behind it was to go from strength to strength.

It was because of the high demand for rabbits that other wares had to be discontinued, and very few of these other items were produced after 1960. Consequently, those early pieces are very collectable as their production span was very short. More and more orders came in and soon the garden shed days became just fond memories as larger premises had to be acquired. From the garden shed they went to Parker Dixons shop, and from thence to the Old Co-operative Grocery Store, to Oxford Mill, to Brennand Mill, and finally in 1973 to Cameron Mill, their current home. PenDelfin bought this mill just twenty years on from the garden shed days, and it was a final indication, if any were needed, that what had started as a hobby was now a highly successful international business. At this mill rabbits hopped off the production line, all hand painted with international sparkle and character. That production line is still generating new models of character, maintaining their status as collectables in the modern markets of the 1990s.

Arthur Morley's arrival at PenDelfin in 1971 caused a stir as with him came a new method of casting the models, improving still further the quality of the finished product. Now each piece was produced under a vacuum process that prevented the formation of bubbles on the surface and ensured that each piece was of the same weight. The casting was now flawless and this can be seen for example on **Snuggles** who was first produced in 1958 and is still being produced today. Compare an early example with a modern piece and notice the tiny pitting on the outer blanket – a very minor point for the late 1950's period and something that wouldn't then be questioned – but not right by today's high standards.

Jeannie Todd was to die in 1974, just over twenty years since founding the business with Jean. It must have been a sad occasion, and as Jean wrote in her book, *The PenDelfin Story*, 'She was demanding, exasperating, generous to a fault – and I loved her dearly'.

This event must have had a deep impression on Jean, and by 1976 she had decided to leave the running of the factory to Arthur Morley and pursue a dream that she had always harboured – a move to a beautiful farmstead in remote Welsh countryside. But there was work to be done still, the designs and modelling could be accomplished outside the confines of Cameron Mill. There Jean and Doreen designed, modelled and scribbled over the next fourteen years.

It must have been an idyllic life and one can only imagine at their despair when they received a message one day in 1988 that the PenDelfin factory had been burned to the ground. The fire crews from Burnley, Nelson, Padiham, Colne and Accrington had all been called in to fight the blaze but it was many hours before it was under control. Over one million pounds of damage had been wrecked on the site and virtually nothing remained. Or so it seemed. Arthur Morely may have initially thought that this was the end of the factory, but less than one week after the fire he had managed to get production under way once more. In the vestages of the ruins essential moulds had remained untouched, and some equipment had also survived. Using a part of the building in which work could continue, the staff rescued what they could, they 'made do', and worked on top of one another in a confined space in order that production of PenDelfin rabbits could continue.

What was to prove beyond salvage was the archive material going back to the earliest days of PenDelfin. Designs, original models, records of sales and milestones of the success of the company had been lost for good. This is why some of the dates we use in this book may not be entirely accurate – we have had to approximate the dates used in some cases.

The studios were rebuilt splendidly in 1987, and it was through the committment of the staff of the company that it had survived to see that day.

Nearly ten years later, with more and more models being designed by Jean Walmsley Heap and Doreen Noel Roberts, PenDelfin still offer their collectors an individualised perspective of human nature through their Rabbit Family, and the homes in which they live, with a freshness of appeal that will surely endure.

Jean Walmsley Heap

Doreen Noel Roberts

9

Three Women, One Man and a Spirited Team

Jean Walmsley Heap, book illustrator, designer, artist and Fellow of the Royal Society of Arts. An extraordinary woman, born in Burnley, Lancashire in the old coaching inn the *Tim Bobbin*. It is still a public house today, proudly displaying a blue plaque issued by Burnley Borough Council in honour of what Jean has done for the town. From the age of four Jean showed an aptitude in art and held the promise of the future in her activites – painting and modelling, concentrating on these throughout her school years. This talent blossomed under her mentor, Noel H Leaver, a very distinguished artist who encouraged Jean in her artistic endeavours. This spurred Jean in the realm of creating her own books and illustrating them. Around 1949 *Dingleflop Chimes* was released, followed by *Dinglefop Moon* in around 1953. These are of course out of print now and are very rare to find, as are the various other books that she illustrated in the 1950s.

Having contributed to the war effort, Jean was commissioned to cheer up the bleak walls of wartime nurseries by the Canadian Red Cross. With her cheerful designs she brought the walls to life, and I am sure that if they were here today, they would have a story to tell, such is her gift for narrative through design. In 1953 she joined the Burnley Building society on a part-time basis to create displays for the publicity department. That is also the year that Jean met Jeannie Todd, and the 'Clay Bashing' hobby began.

Jeannie Todd was introduced to Jean by Noel Leaver at the building society, she too being local to the area, being born in Worsthorne, a tiny village on the outskirts of Burnley. They discovered a kindred spirit and over a cup of tea on a stormy day in a wooden hut the idea of PenDelfin was born.

Jeannie was most notable for her drive and efficiency. Not for her the idea of putting things off until tomorrow, her motto soon became a byword for the company – 'Do it Now'. The name was indeed a combination of the Pendle setting in which they found themselves and the 'elfin' like quality of

Pendle Witch plaque. Introduced 1953, withdrawn 1957. Market value £1500-£2000.

Fairy Shop plaque. Introduced 1954, withdrawn 1958. Market value £1500-£2500.

the work they were to undertake. Almost overnight, they were up and running, with the name registered and the hut commandeered for work.

Jeannie took on the task of mould making and casting while Jean concentrated on the design and modelling. With little but enthusiasm to keep them going they made the first of today's collectables, the **Pendle Witch** plaque, and **The Fairy Shop**. It was not all plain sailing, as evidenced by more of Jeannie's mottos – 'From Small Beginnings' was accompanied with 'By Error We Progress'.

A year later the dynamic duo were ready to take on extra help in the form of Doreen Noel Roberts. She was taken into the fold to take charge of the small number of part-time staff that were working. At least they were being paid, for the partners struggling to set up the business there was often nothing at all! Doreen soon learned all the processes that were involved in manufacture in the fledgeling company – casting, trimming, shading, tinting, glossing, gilding, packing, and, with the help of Jean, unblocking the drains. (Something I'm sure she must smile about now and again as they reflect on the past.)

In 1955 success necessitated a move from the Parker Dixon shop which had been the first tentative step from the garden shed. They were now at the Old Co-operative grocery store. All three women had untold pleasure knowing their hobby had now become a business. The same year saw their first exhibition which was held at the Blackpool International Trade Fair. Their success was in finding a new sales team – Greta Godbold and Mr Rawlins. With orders subsequently coming in from them they had as much work as they could cope with. The quality of hand-finishing and painting was now being appreciated in department stores and gift shops up and down the country.

Things proceeded apace for the next ten years or so, with management staff expanding further with Doris Simm's arrival. In 1968 Jeannie suffered a broken hip and was in and out of hospital with it over a couple of years. Doris had been Painting Supervisor and went to Head of Studios, working with Doreen on the production side.

The success of PenDelfin was all the more remarkable for its having an executive team that was exclusively women. In this industrious cotton town it would have been unthinkable that a team of women would become the driving force behind one of the biggest commercial success stories the town had ever known. This was well before the advent of feminism and one can only guess at some of the patronising attitudes they must have endured along the way. In fact it may be safe to say that the fame of the company was eclipsed only by the notoriety of that other bastion of Burnley male pride – the local football team, which up until the mid 1970s struck fear into the souls of their nearest rivals at Manchester United before descending gracefully to the lower divisions.

By the early seventies though, the ladies of PenDelfin decided to call upon the services of a certain gentleman – Arthur M. Morley. An engineer by trade, Arthur had watched the progress of the company with keen interest. Arthur was notified of casting problems that caused bubbling as air collected in the rubber moulds when the slip was poured into them. These not only created wastage and flaws in the surface, but meant inconsistency in the end products that were being produced. In a matter of months Mr Morley produced a machine that would produce flawless casts under vacuum which would ensure that these production problems would no longer occur. The facility for flawless casting was to prove a real boon and soon Mr Morley became an integral part of the team. In 1972 he was appointed Director, and in 1975 Managing Director. Mr Morley was now ensuring the continued success of the PenDelfin company whilst Jean and Doreen moved to Wales and a more congenial environment for their creative designs.

PenDelfin Variants

PenDelfin have introduced a number of items that are not strictly part of the range but for which their characters have formed a basis.

PenDelfin Charms

These little miniature models of six of the rabbit characters were made from solid Sterling Silver, in Canada. Approximately 300 sets were made and distributed to H Birks Ltd in Canada and the

Left: Phumf charm.. 10mm 1979-1980. £80-£120
Right: Muncher charm 10mm 1979-1980. £80-£120

U.S.A. They were not produced in the United Kingdom due to an increase in Sterling Silver prices which would have made the charms uneconomical to produce. Barney was made in 15 ct gold as well though – in a very limited edition of just six – and it is consequently extremely rare.

Metallion Range

The range of Metallion sculpture began in 1980 and was continued only until 1985. All the items were designed by Jean Walmsley Heap and Doreen Noel Roberts. PenDelfin Sculpture Ltd. worked from the Welsh Studios producing ware that had a patina of bronze and the meticulous detail of an original antique bronze sculpture.

While this provided a welcome departure from the normal concentration on rabbits, it was soon realised that this range was not going to be a success, and the project was dropped. Needless to say, these items are now quite rare and so collectors have bid up prices on them. However, it must be noted that there

Elf Tree flower holder. 4inches high £300-£500

Rose Dragon. 18inches high, £1500-£2000

Dragon candle holder 4 inches high. £150-£250

Left: Swan Child wall sculpture. Right: Ivy Leaf posy holder and matching candlestick.

are a number of seconds on the market and it can be difficult to tell them apart. Look out for the lack of patina – a slightly dull finish as opposed to a shiny bronze finish. The seconds did not have as much bronze content as the firsts and the bronze coating is not as thick. Seconds still have value though – it is just a question of knowing what you are buying and getting the right price.

Collectors Plates and China Wares.
The range of Collectors Plates comprises of six designs, all limited editions. They were produced by commission in fine bone china by Royal Grafton and the Elizabethan Bone China Works.

Each plate carries an individual number and is issued with a certificate of authenticity. Three of the plates are now out of production and reach much higher prices than those at which they were issued. The three that are left are bound to go the same way!

The other fine bone china items are not produced as limited editions and are available at your nearest stockist. Don't be deceived though, if they are discontinued at some future date they are bound to become as collectable as the other products.

These items tend to be produced with either blue or pink highlighted rims and consist of breakfast sets, mugs, a tea for two set and small, medium or large trinket boxes. All these items are detailed with PenDelfin rabbits in various designs, made by Sevarg.

The Caravan (PenDelfin exclusive).

14

The Old Schoolhouse plate.

Gingerbread Day plate

Pictures and Books

The block mounted wall pictures are illustrations from books, capturing a moment in the story. They are now out of production but the literary joy can be captured by reading the three PenDelfin *Village Tales* by Jean and Doreen – *Barney* and his flying adventure, *Whopper* and his mysterious catch, and *The Family* with its mischievous and entertaining characters. All published in 1987 and 1988, they make interesting reading for adults and children alike.

Repaints and Restorations

Like all items in ceramics or stonecraft, there are vulnerable elements on the PenDelfin range. If knocked to the ground the model may be chipped or may even lose an ear or an arm. It is therefore possible to find pieces that have been restored or repainted. If this is the case, the work done does not necessarily maintain the value of a perfect original. A figure which is slightly chipped or has a glaze flake is in many ways more desirable than a restored piece, due to its originality. Even when repaints are executed in the same colourway as the original, they never look 'quite' the same. Age shows on a model and adds to its charm, and it can be quite acceptable for a model that is 30 years old to have some sort of fault or other. However, a genuine model which has stood the test of time (and the mantle piece), is most desirable in perfect condition, especially the models that were top-heavy, for example, **Father Rabbit, Megan the Harp** and **Cha Cha** have a tendency to fall over and it is rare to see a piece that does not have some damage.

PenDelfin have offered a service to restore and repaint models at the studios. In order to do this they strip the figure or model completely and more or less start from scratch. This makes the figure look like new when completed, but it somehow looks odd to see an old figure in new paints – and in fact the recipe for these paints has changed over the years, giving a bolder finish than the early subtle tones that prevailed at the time.

The more casual approach to production in the early days has made for some very interesting and varied examples which may become valuable in the future, and they have certainly led to collectors buying more than one of the same model. It will be down to the next edition of this book to see if any have emerged with extra value.

Cauldron Witch, Left: Stripped ready for re-painting and right, how it should look.

Bandstand, Thumper and Piano Clanger; Jingle; Phumf; Rocky Casanova; Bongo, Bongo.

17

Forty Winks, introduced 1993, withdrawn 1995 £30-£50; Teddy, introduced 1995; Twins, introduced 1962.

Wakey, introduced 1958; Parsley, introduced 1987; Snuggles, introduced 1958; Peeps, introduced 1966.

18

Toy Shop, introduced 1992; Jacky, introduced 1992; Honey, introduced 1989, withdrawn 1992, £30-£50.

The Old School House; Solo; Digit; Euclid; Newboy; Wordsworth; Duffy.

Humphrey Go Kart, introduced 1988, withdrawn 1994, £40-£60; Birdie, introduced 1987; Rambler, introduced 1991; Dobbin, introduced 1995; Tennyson, introduced 1987, withdrawn 1994, £40-£60.

Chirpy, introduced 1989, withdrawn 1992, £40-£60.

Victoria, introduced 1986.

Forty Winks, introduced 1993, withdrawn 1995, £30-£50.

Dodger, introduced 1964, withdrawn 1995, £30-£50.

Robins Cave, introduced in 1995.

Crocker, introduced 1980, withdrawn 1989, £30-£40.

Caravan (PenDelphin exclusive), introduced 1976.

Raft, introduced 1983; Jim Lad, introduced 1986, withdrawn 1992, £60-£100.

Jetty, introduced 1979; Whopper, introduced 1979; Bosun, introduced 1992, withdrawn 1993, £60-£100.

Picnic Island, Muncher; Picnic Basket, Robert (Lollipop); Pieface; Picnic Midge.

Scout, introduced 1992; Camp Fire, introduced 1993.

Shrimp Stand, introduced 1966, withdrawn 1982; Little Mo, Introduced 1986, withdrawn 1994, £30-£40; Nipper, introduced 1986, withdrawn 1994, £30-£40.

Castle Tavern, introduced 1968.

Cobble Cottage, introduced 1967.

The Large House, introduced 1966.

Mother (2nd version), introduced 1977.

Father (3rd version), introduced 1977.

Aunt Ruby, limited edition 10,000, introduced 1993, withdrawn 1996, £100-£200.

Cousin Beau, introduced 1993.

Bellman (membership gift), introduced
January 1995, withdrawn December 1996,
£50-£80.

Herald (founder member), introduced
October 1992, withdrawn December 1993.
£70-£100.

Buttons (membership gift) introduced
January 1994, withdrawn December 1994,
£50-£80.

Newsie (membership gift), introduced
January 1996, withdrawn December 1996,
£30-£50.

Puffer, Model of the Year 1994, £50-£80.

Delia, Model of the Year 1996.

George & Dragon, Model of the Year 1995,
£50-£80

Bosun, Model of the Year 1992, £60-£100.

Butterfingers, introduced 1991.

Angelo, introduced 1990.

Jacky, introduced 1992.

Crocker, introduced 1980, withdrawn 1989, £30-£40.

Clanger, introduced 1983.

Thumper and Piano, introduced 1967.

Rocky (1st version), introduced 1959,
withdrawn 1978, £30-£50.

Bongo, introduced 1964, withdrawn 1987,
£40-£60.

34

Phumph, introduced 1967, withdrawn 1985, £50-£80.

Rosa, introduced 1982.

Solo, introduced 1985, withdrawn 1993 £40-£60.

Roll, introduced 1959.

Dandy, introduced 1981.

Pipkin, introduced 1994.

Honey, introduced 1989, withdrawn 1992, £30-£50.

New Boy, introduced 1990.

36

Mike, introduced 1994.

Jingle, introduced 1985, withdrawn 1992, £40-£60.

Tippit, introduced 1995.

Wordsworth, introduced 1991, withdrawn 1993, £60-£100.

Boswell, introduced 1972.

Nipper, introduced 1981, withdrawn 1989, £60-£100.

Blossom, introduced 1984, withdrawn 1989, £40-£60.

Scrumpy, introduced 1985; Apple Barrel, introduced 1985, withdrawn 1992, £20-£30.

The Kitchen, introduced 1995; Charlotte, introduced 1990, withdrawn 1992, £50-£80; Cheeky, introduced 1996; Scoffer, introduced 1991; Delia, Model of the Year 1996-1977.

The Kitchen, introduced 1995; Cookie, introduced 1995; Pepper, introduced 1995; Oliver, introduced 1984, withdrawn 1985, £40-£50; Butterfingers, introduced 1991.

Barney, introduced 1967; Bath, introduced 1967, withdrawn 1975, £40-£60; Totty, introduced 1971, withdrawn 1981, £50-£80; Dandy, introduced 1981.

Blossom, introduced 1984, withdrawn 1989, £40-£60; Moppit, introduced 1996.

Picnic stand,1965, withdrawn 1985, £80-£120; Maud, introduced 1967, withdrawn 1978, £100-£200; Mike, introduced 1994; Rosa, introduced 1982; Rolly, introduced 1959.

Runaway, introduced and withdrawn 1995, £60-£100; Walmsley, introduced and withdrawn 1994, £80-£120; 1996 Event Piece.

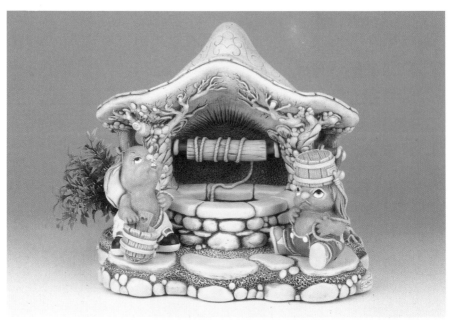

Wishing Well, introduced 1994; Pipkin, introduced 1994; and Tippit, introduced 1995.

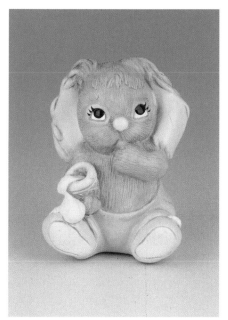

Vanilla, introduced 1993.

Sunny, introduced 1992.

Maud, introduced 1967, withdrawn 1978,
£100-£200.

Big Spender, introduced 1996.

43

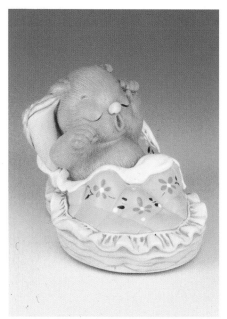

Snuggles Awake, introduced, 1991.

Rambler, introduced 1991.

Birdie, introduced 1987.

*Humphrey Go Kart, introduced 1988,
withdrawn 1994, £40-£60.*

Father (Dungaree), introduced 1955, withdrawn 1960, £700-£1000; Mother (thin neck), introduced and withdrawn 1956, £250-£300.

Father (Kipper tie), introduced 1960, withdrawn 1970, £400-£600; Mother, introduced 1956, withdrawn 1978, £200-£400.

Aunt Agatha, rare, introduced 1963, withdrawn 1965, £1000-£1500.

Cyril Squirrel, very rare, introduced 1963, withdrawn 1965, £1000-£2000.

Gallery plaque 'Pieface'.

Gallery plaque 'Wakey'.

Gallery plaque 'Poppet'.

Gallery plaque 'Dodger'.

Gallery plaque 'Robert'.

Gallery plaque.

Gallery plaques were introduced in 1968, withdrawn 1971, £150-£200 each.

Miniature "A" wall plaques; Topper; Balloon Woman; Flying Witch; Bellman. They are rare and were introduced in 1955, withdrawn 1956, and market value is £400-£600 each.

Romeo and Juliet plaques (ivory), rare, introduced 1957, withdrawn 1959, £1500-£2000.

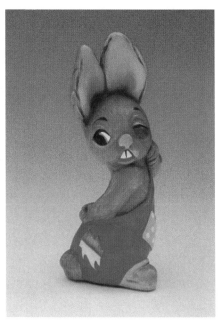

Shiner, introduced 1960, withdrawn 1967, £300-£400.

Robert (1st version), introduced 1956, withdrawn 1967, £180-£240.

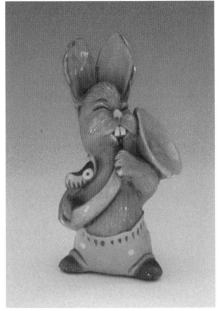

Lucy Pocket, introduced 1960, withdrawn 1967, £80-£120.

Cha Cha, rare, introduced 1959, withdrawn 1961, £1000-£1500

Squeezy, introduced 1960, withdrawn 1970, £250-£350.

Megan the Harp. introduced 1960, withdrawn 1967, £200-£400.

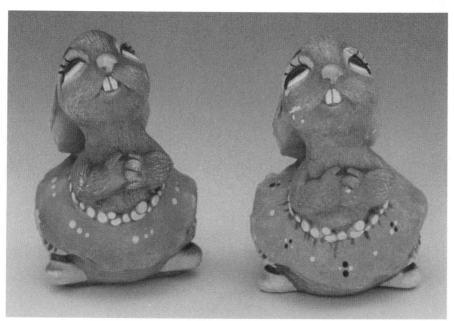

Margot (2nd versions), introduced 1957, withdrawn 1967, £80-£120.

Model stand, introduced 1960, withdrawn 1967, £200-£400.

Model stand used for display purposes, introduced 1960, withdrawn 1967, £150-£250.

Picnic stand, introduced 1965, withdrawn 1985, £80-£120.

Timber stand, introduced 1966, withdrawn 1982, £40-£60.

Shrimp stand, introduced 1966, withdrawn 1982, £60-£100.

Picnic Island, introduced 1985, still in production.

Grandstand (1st version), introduced 1961, withdrawn 1969, £100-£200.

Mouse House, introduced 1964, withdrawn 1969, £300-£500.

Cornish Prayer, introduced 1962,
withdrawn 1965, £400-£600.

Manx Kitten, very rare, introduced 1956,
withdrawn 1958, £1800-£2500.

Uncle Soames, can be found in numerous
colourways, introduced 1959, withdrawn
1985, £150-£250.

Balcony scene, introduced 1982, still
current.

Tipsy Witch, introduced 1953, withdrawn 1959, £300-£500; Cauldron Witch, introduced 1953, withdrawn 1959, £600-£800.

Left: Mother Mouse; Father Mouse; Lollipop Mouse (grey). Right: Mother Mouse; Father Mouse; Lollipop Mouse (brown). Introduced 1961, withdrawn 1966, estimates range from £300-£800.

Muncher, introduced 1965, withdrawn
1983, £60-£100 and Cake Stand.

Picnic Table.

Milk Jug Stand, introduced 1966,
withdrawn 1972, £300-£500

Cake Stand, introduced 1966, withdrawn
1972, £250-£300.

Pendle Witch plaque, introduced 1953, withdrawn 1957, £1500-£2000.

Metallion Pendle Witch plaque, introduced 1980, withdrawn 1985, £500-£800.

The Fruit Shop, introduced 1968; Barrowboy, introduced 1968.

Christmas scene, limited edition of 2000, introduced 1985, withdrawn 1986, £500-£1000.

Old Meg plaque, very rare, introduced 1953, withdrawn 1954, £2000-£3000

Shaggy Dog plaque, very rare, introduced 1960, withdrawn 1961, £500-£800.

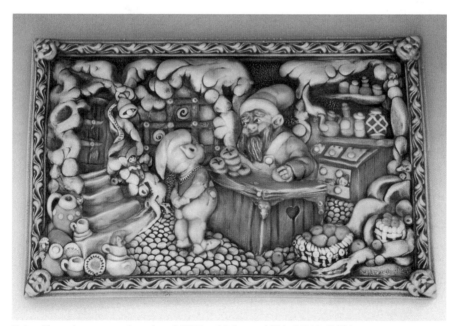

Fairy Shop plaque, rare, introduced 1954, withdrawn 1958, £1500-£2000.

Mother and Baby plate, introduced 1982, withdrawn 1983, £70-£100.

Father plate, limited edition of 10000, introduced 1982, withdrawn 1984, £60-£100.

The Dance, 14in x 20in, introduced 1989, withdrawn 1994, £30-£40.

The Homestead, 14in x 20in, introduced 1989, withdrawn 1994, £30-£50.

The Auction, 14in x 20in, introduced 1989, withdrawn 1994, £30-£40.

Whopper at Cobble Cottage plate, limited edition of 7500, introduced 1982, withdrawn 1985, £60-£100.

59

Aunt Ruby colourway model.

Original Father, circa 1955

Three colourways of Rambler.

Daisy Duck, rare, introduced 1955, withdrawn 1958, £800-£1200.

Pooch, introduced 1967, withdrawn 1987, £50-£80; Tammy, introduced 1957, withdrawn 1987, £50-£80.

Rabbit bookends, rare, introduced 1958, withdrawn 1965, £3000-£5000.

Poppet, introduced 1964, still current.

Picnic Basket, introduced 1966, withdrawn 1968, £300-£500.

Metallion Elf Tree candle holder, introduced 1980, withdrawn 1985, £150-£250.

Metallion Shell flower holder, introduced 1980, withdrawn 1985, £180-£240.

Metallion Dove chalice, introduced 1980, withdrawn 1985, £300-£500.

Metallion Rabbit bookends, introduced 1980, withdrawn 1985, £800-£1200.

Variations of Colour and Decoration

'How many colourways are there of this?' This is a question that can be asked on many occasions when visiting large collections with lots of variations on display. You will not just see one **Lucy Pocket**, for instance, but twenty or more, all different with eyes that may be looking in different directions or even a slightly different facial expression. Or she could have an expression of deep thought, or her pocket may be painted with a patched work design or a floral spray.

This range of colour can be a starting point in many collections. **Uncle Soames** can drive a collector to despair, such are the wide range of dandy cravats and dapper waistcoats he posesses. His attire started off in natural shades of beige and black, but soon the paintresses decided to liven him up a bit. He was then painted with bright blue or yellow waistcoats with speckled cravats, or a black waistcoat and multicolour splashes. The rarest **Uncle Soames** is therefore the one in ordinary brown trousers – the most sombre of the versions.

Aunt Agatha however (that flighty rabbit who was married to **Uncle Soames** and ran off with **Cyril Squirrel**) is most desired in blue. While the colourway of black, pink and turquoise picks out her independent spirit, the blue colourway gives her an air of elegance. With yellow, black and red details, this is the one to find for your collection. If you collect **Aunt Agatha** then one of each colour is a must. There may also be other colourways – early on in the years of production, the painting procedure was much more informal and a 'one off' is quite likely.

Colourways vary on numerous models and on these there are too many to list or take account of. Applied or inscribed decoration also varies – **Rolly** may have a treble cleft or a single cleft on his song sheet – the piano may only have two swags inscribed or numerous flowers with foliage. The leaves in **Barrow Boy's** cart may be two, or three and so on. A modelling change is more significant. For instance the bell that **Jingle** holds may be small or large. This is because when Doreen was looking at this piece in the factory one day, she decided a large bell would look better. She promptly made the larger bell and this was re-moulded and a new piece made. Consequently, collectors look out for both models.

The value of models in terms of colourway is difficult to assess. With such a complexity of different colours on different models it is also quite a task to find out which ones are the rare colours and which ones are the most common. For example, **Rosa** was painted in blue in the first few years, but then she changed to pink. There are probably greater numbers in pink, but her value is not affected by this at the current time. In the next few years, as the secondary market develops, colourways may become more important, but at the moment, it does not generally affect the value.

Recorded variations of colour

These are the known variations of colour that were officially sanctioned by PenDelfin. If you have a piece that is not in one of these variations than you may have a 'one-off'.

Angelo	Blue/Turquoise/Green
Barney	Black/Blue, Black/Red, Black/Turquoise
Barrow Boy	Blue, Turquoise, Green
Birdie	Pink, Blue, Kingfisher
Bobby	Christmas Colours
Boswell	Red, Green, Blue
Butterfingers	Blue, Turquoise
Casanova	Blue, Red, Green
Charlotte	Turquoise/Pink/Blue
Chirpy	Pink, Blue
Clanger	Blue, Red, Green
Cousin Beau	Baby Colourway
Dandy	Blue only
Digit	Red, Turquoise, Dark Blue
Dobbin	Red, Eye Blue, Pale Turquoise
Dodger	Yellow/Blue, Yellow/Kingfisher, Turquoise/Black, Red/Green
Duffy	Pink, Green, Green (shoes)
Euclid	Blue, Red, Kingfisher
Father	Pale Green/Dark Green (one colour)
Forty Winks	Pale Turquoise/Kingfisher, Blue/Pale Pink, Blue
Honey	Mid Blue, Dark Blue, Turquoise, Red Feet
Humphrey Go Kart	Green, Blue, Turquoise
Jacky	Pink, Turquoise, Blue (shoes)
Jim Lad	Black, Turquoise, Blue
Jingle	Red, Blue, Pink, Turquoise
Little Mo	Red/Green, Turquoise/Kingfisher, Blue/Dark Blue
Midge (Picnic)	Red, Green, Blue
Mike	Black, Blue, Pale Turquoise

New Boy	Turquoise/Blue/Red
Oliver	Red, Blue, Green
Parsley	Blue, Pink/Turquoise
Peeps	Pink/Turquoise, Blue, Pink, Green
Pepper	Blue, Pale Pink, Pale Turquoise
Pipkin	Red, Turquoise, Blue
Poppet	Blue, Pink, Green, Blue/Black
Rambler	Blue/Red/Pale Turquoise
Rocky	Red/Green, Pink, Blue, Kingfisher
Rosa	Pink
Scoffer	Green, Blue, Turquoise (shoes)
Scout	Red, Blue
Scrumpy	Green, Blue, Turquoise
Snuggles	Blue, Pink, Green, Blue/Black
Snuggles (Awake)	Solid Pink patchwork, Blue/Turquoise, Black/Green patchwork
Solo	Red, Blue, Pink, Turquoise
Sunny	Cas Blue/Ord Blue/Pale Turquoise, Icing Pink/Pale Turquoise
Teddy	Blue, Pale Turquoise/Pale Pink
Tennyson	Turquoise, Kingfisher, Blue, Dark Blue
Thumper	Red, Green, Blue
Tiddler	(All black shoes), Blue Eye, Red/Pale Turquoise
Tippit	Red, Blue, Turquoise
Twins	Turquoise/Pink, Blue, Black/Blue
Vanilla	Red, Blue, Turquoise
Victoria	Red/Blue cover, Blue/Blue cover, Turquoise/Yellow cover
Wakey	Blue, Pink, Green, Pink/Turquoise
Whopper	Blue
Wordsworth	Red/Turquoise/Blue

Process and Progress

Designers, Jean Walmsley Heap and Doreen Noel Roberts deliberate over each new model. It is not until they have carefully considered the appropriateness of a new idea that they go ahead – each with a new design. Sketches are made showing various angles and facial expressions – until the new characters (now with names!) begin to emerge – as true members of the PenDelfin family.

View of PenDelfin's Studio

Once modelled in clay , the figure is ready to be copied into a master mould. A special thick white jelly substance set around the clay model, and when it sets it retains all the details of the original. If this were ceramic material, a lot of the detail would be lost, but by this process, even a thumb-print on the figure is copied. (If one was left on it, which I doubt!).

This master mould then forms the basis for new moulds to be made into which the special stonecraft material can be poured. This is called casting. The cream liquid material has the consistency of milk when poured, but in only a few minutes it sets, as if by magic, into thick, heavy stonecraft.

In the old days the pouring would lead to air bubbles and variations in weight, but in the 1970s, Arthur Morley found the solution by developing a machine that would pour under vacuum, so that no air bubbles were possible. This kept PenDelfin in the frame as a high quality producer, with a finish that was superior to other manufacturers.

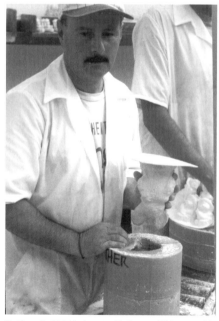

Father Rabbit being pulled out of his mould.

Group of small figures being pulled from their moulds

The first item to be painted is the colour prototype. A number of pieces are sent back to the studio for Jean or Doreen to paint up, so that the painters can start production. The chosen prototype is returned to the factory on a wooden plinth, and this piece is the final colour trial to which the painters have to refer.

Once cast, the production models are then trimmed so that no seams are visible.

Thus cleaned up, they are dipped in a solution which seals them so that they are no longer porous.

After this, they are stained all over in a beige colour. This colouring runs into crevices in the modelling and highlights the features of the model. The excess over the body is wiped away so that only a faint colouring is left there, contrasting with the darker shading.

From thence the model is sent for 'pinking and tinting' in which colours like the pink of the inner ears are picked out and other tints are applied where necessary.

This is only the beginning. From here the pieces go to the individual Painters for the exacting application of solid

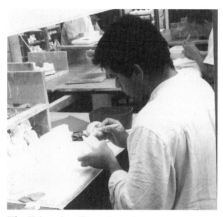

The Trimming Department – seams are settled away.

The Dipping Rack.

Before and after the first colouring. Note that the eyes and other details have been wiped over to give depoth of colour and highlight the modelling.

colour (pants, coats, shoes, etc) in the precise shades decreed by the designers . . .

Finally – the intricate work of the Decorators for decorative flowers or swirls – and the various expressions in the eyes. The work of each PenDelfin artist can be immediately recognised by eagle-eyed Supervisors.

After painting the models are dried and then applied with a protective semi-matt glaze with maybe an additional gloss highlight. The final touch is a fitted green baize with a black and gilt paper label with the model's name on it and the PenDelfin logo. Finally, it is packed in the familiar turquoise and black gift-box. Technology can speed up output, but as quality is the key word at PenDelfin, the traditional methods still apply and even though one model can take up to a week to complete the model is one hundred per cent finished, and finished to the highest standard. Cameron Mill is leagues away from the garden shed days but the mottos of days gone by still remain – 'Do it now!' is one that will always remain.

Decorating details like eyes is a very skilled job.

Rows and rows of the finished pieces being dried off after laquering.

Painting. Where all the basic colours are applied.

Finally, after the baize and backstamp are applied, they are packed into boxes.

The Most Elusive Pieces

Every collector craves a rare or interesting piece to add to their collection, and it may take months or even years of collecting to find that piece at the right price. It may be at a fair, or an auction or a boot sale , or even a jumble sale. Rare items can turn up at almost any time in the most unlikely of places. Any collector who has been at it long enough will have a tale to tell about a certain 'find'.

On top of this there are the highly elusive prototypes or items produced in very short production runs. These are models that were made at the PenDelfin Studios at an early stage, but were not put into production. If you find a piece of PenDelfin which is not recorded in this book, you may have one of these models, but you must beware. The piece would have to be authenticated by the PenDelfin Studios. Very often people pick a piece from a rival producer and assume that it is a rare piece of PenDelfin – so be careful!

Among the rare models that have been authenticated are unnamed seated dogs, wearing scarves and berets. These were made in the 1960s and are very rare. There was also a shaggy dog wall plaque that again was produced in 1960 and had a very short production run. These were approximately five inches high and if found would be quite valuable (see illustration). **Old Meg** is another wall plaque. She is five inches high and just under four inches wide, superbly modelled with a life-like expression. **Old Meg** turned up unexpectedly and caused quite a stir at the PenDelfin Studios when Jean saw it and identified it as one she had made many years ago and had forgotten all about. There must be more out there – do you have one?

Early prototypes are essential for collectors who wish to have the complete collection. Viewing at auction for one of these pieces is inevitable and if two avid collectors are in the same showroom, dramatic prices can be realised. It is possible therefore that some of these very early pieces could reach unexpected heights in the next few years.

Top ten most sought after pieces:

1) Manx Kitten

2) Daisy Duck

3) Bobbin Woman

4) Cyril Squirrel

5) Rabbit Bookends

6) Desmond Duck

7) Fairy Shop Plaque

8) Nursery Rhyme Plaques

9) 'Gallery Series' of five 'framed' figures; Wakey, Dodger, Robert, Poppet, Pieface (with easel wedge).

10) Manx Pixie, *Phynnodderee* and assorted small plaques 'Miniature A' set of six

This range of top ten most sought after pieces doesn't necessarily mean they are the rarest. Collectors want specific items to complete or add to their collections and over the recent months before publication of this book, I have gauged how interested collectors are in these items. One to note is **Bobbin Woman**, who is extremely rare. As only two are known, it is difficult to imagine that we will ever see one on the open market. It won't stop us looking though will it?

The Hunt for Little Thrifty

Little Thrifty is a character that was prominent in the Children's Corner at the Burnley Building Society. Stories by Jean Walmsley Heap centred around the character of Little Thrifty, and a large model of him was commissioned. It is the largest of the models made by Jean, and since it caused quite a few problems, no other models on that scale have been attempted since.

Little Thrifty took pride of place at the Easter Parade and was then re-sited at the Burnley Building Society offices. With subsequent changes within the organisation, **Little Thrifty** has been lost – but PenDelfin would be overjoyed to find what has happened to him – do you know?

How to Identify PenDelfin

Imitation, they say, is the highest form of flattery. Whenever success becomes apparent, someone somewhere will always want to jump on the bandwaggon. These people could be seen as opportunists, but in a market economy, it could be argued that it is perfectly natural for competition to spring up. It is healthy for competitors to compete, thus ensuring that the best outcome for the consumer is a product that is the best quality, at the lowest prices.

When PenDelfin set up their studios in the 1950s they were completely unique. When success came their way, competitors tried to imitate the style and composition of the range. The world is full of stories of companies which have initiated a product, only to find that a bigger company has 'taken them on' and swamped the market with their own, very similar product. But not with PenDelfin. Imitators have been and gone, and PenDelfin have established their superiority and their price competitiveness over forty years.

So we have established that competition is healthy, and that PenDelfin have achieved a great deal by surviving and growing in spite of this. There is nothing wrong in finding pieces of stonecraft look-a-like rabbits that have a different backstamp on the base. The thing that collectors must beware of, is finding a rabbit that has had a PenDelfin backstamp put on it when it shouldn't be there – or, more importantly, finding a rabbit that does not have a backstamp at all, and assuming it to be PenDelfin.

If this book serves no other purpose than to put right the misconceptions of collectors over what is and what is not PenDelfin, it will have done its job. Unfortunately, there are quite a number of collectors who have a rogue piece in their collections!

An example of a Moorcraft model, Two Rabbits in a Jug, note the more comic expressions with buck teeth and plump jowls.

The backstamp beneath shows a gilt and black paper label, very similar to PenDelfin's.

What to look for

Glaze
The finish on PenDelfin is a semi-matt glaze. In other words, there is a certain dullness to the finish, giving a more life-like effect to the piece. Certain items on the piece may be picked out in a gloss finish, like the pupils, but you will not find a rabbit with a purely glossed finish all-over. If you have one, it is probably not PenDelfin.

Modelling
The modelling of a PenDelfin rabbit is always superior. The artistry of Jean Walmsley Heap and Doreen Noel Roberts is way ahead of the rivals. If your 'PenDelfin' piece is poorly modelled, it will not be from that factory – it will be from some other! Things to look out for are the definition of the facial features, for example, a lack of raised eyebrows or no creases in the cheeks. Also, is the composition of the piece – the stance, expression and items within it – what you would expect?

Paintwork
On non-PenDelfin, the paintwork is likely to be inferior. Many of the imitators have tried to skimp on the superior production and finish of PenDelfin (obviously hoping to undercut them on price to the retailer). The paintwork is often applied very thinly and lacks a tinted base coat. Also, the paint detail tends to be significantly inferior, with the brown of the rabbit fur being much more orangey than the PenDeflin rabbit. PenDelfin often has little flowers or patterns carefully painted at strategic points, and there are variations of tone and colour that are applied at the 'pinking and tinting' stage. Does the item you are looking at have that 'quality' feel?

The Base
The base of the PenDelfin range changed after 1970. Up to then they are solid, but thereafter, they have a hole in the base which is covered by the baize (usually green). If the item has a label, beware that unscrupulous people may have applied it in order to deceive. The particular backstamps that PenDelfin have used are important to note, and for that we have devoted a separate chapter.

Imitation pieces do not bear a hole to the base whereas a piece of post-1970's PenDelfin does – this is due to being put on a dipping rack. The significance is that a collector should feel the base, it should have a hole in it, if it hasn't it may not be genuine.

Backstamps and Labels

The dating of labels is very difficult as the most accurate information was contained in records that were destroyed in the fire of the mid-1980s. Therefore some of our guides are only approximate.

The labels have common features. They are generally paper with a black background and gold inscription. However, they come in various shapes which incorporate a variety of wording which may or may not include:

PenDelfin name
Registered Trademark
Handpainted Stonecraft
Made in England
Characters Name.

On early models 'designed by Jean Walmsley Heap' may be inscribed as with the gilt Butterfly label.

The Membership Gifts and Model of the Year figures bear black circular labels with gold inscriptions.

The Pre 1960s plaques, for example **Pendle Witch** or the **Fairy Shop** have handpainted titles and Jean Walmsley Heap's signature. These are not backed with baize.

Handpainted signature and Logo, titled, painted in red circa 1954-1958. Some pieces have subsequently been signed by Jean Walmsley Heap.

Gilt Butterfly label label found on larger, old retired pieces such as Old Mother, Original Grandstand and Bandstand. Circa 1956-1960.

Label found on Cornish Prayer along with traditional label, circa 1962-1965.

White artist palette label with gold print. Only found on Rocky and Wakey so far. Origin unknown, circa 1960-1962.

Rectangular gold (circa 1958-1970) or silver (circa 1958-1960) foil label with black lettering found on smaller, old retired pieces such as Gussie, Original Robert, Shiner. Also found on a few larger ones as well such as Uncle Soames.

Three labels based on the artist palette label format: The first two are traditional black labels with gold foil border, containing the name of the piece. It is found on most pieces. Circa 1960-1980s. Far right has "Regd Design" instead of the name of the piece and is found on some early models.

Left: Black label but without gold foil border. Found on a few of older retired pieces.

Right: Triangle shaped label, black with white print.

Listings

Rabbits

To begin with, just five rabbits came into life – **Father**, **Mother**, **Robert**, **Margot**, and **Midge**. Many colourways can be found on these pieces, so collectors must beware of thinking that a colourway is unique. In some cases these colourways can be highly sought after though. For instance, **Uncle Soames** in brown trousers is very much desired. There may also be a colour variation in Bongo's drum, for example, which when coloured and not black is an earlier version. There is a lot of interest in the more unusual tones, too numerous to mention here, but a separate chapter concentrates on these later in the book.

Because of the characters of PenDelfin Rabbits, it is easy to concoct stories relating to them, and Jean and Doreen did just this with their books in the *Village Tales* series of books. For instance, there is the tale that **Aunt Agatha** ran off with **Cyril Squirrel**, much to the relief of her husband, **Uncle Soames**. There are many more mischievous tales which make not only for interesting reading, but collecting as well!

Mother Rabbit (Thin Neck).
Introduced 1956.
Withdrawn 1956
Market value £250-£300

Father (Dungaree)
Introduced 1955
Withdrawn 1960
Market value £700-£1000

Shiner 1960-1967
£300-£400

Rocky (1st) 1959-1978
£30-£50

Rosa 1982-cur

Squeezy 1960-1970
£250-£350

Robert 1956-1967
£180-£240

Megan the Harp 1960-1967
£200-£400

Angelo Designed by Jean Walmsley Heap

Size	Production dates	Market value		Date acquired	Price paid	
4¼"	1990-Cur	RRP	RRP	_____	_____	☐

Aunt Agatha Designed by Jean Walmsley Heap

Size	Production dates	Market value		Date acquired	Price paid	
8"	1963-1965	£1000-£1500	$2150-$3000	_____	_____	☐

Aunt Ruby Designed by Jean Walmsley Heap
Limited Edition of 10,000

Size	Production dates	Market value		Date acquired	Price paid	
8"	1993-1996	£100-£200	$200-$400	_____	_____	☐

Barney Designed by Doreen Noel Roberts

Size	Production dates	Market value		Date acquired	Price paid	
3"	1967-Cur	RRP	RRP	_____	_____	☐

Barrow Boy Designed by Jean Walmsley Heap

Size	Production dates	Market value		Date acquired	Price paid	
4½"	1968-Cur	RRP	RRP	_____	_____	☐

Big Spender Designed by Doreen Noel Roberts

Size	Production dates	Market value		Date acquired	Price paid	
3¾"	1996-Cur	RRP	RRP	_____	_____	☐

Birdie Designed by Jean Walmsley Heap

Size	Production dates	Market value		Date acquired	Price paid	
4½"	1987-Cur	RRP	RRP	_____	_____	☐

Blossom Designed by Doreen Noel Roberts

Size	Production dates	Market value		Date acquired	Price paid	
4"	1984-1989	£40-£60	$85-$125	_____	_____	☐

Bobby Designed by Doreen Noel Roberts

Size	Production dates	Market value		Date acquired	Price paid	
4½"	1996-Cur	RRP	RRP	_____	_____	☐

Bongo Designed by Jean Walmsley Heap

Size	Production dates	Market value		Date acquired	Price paid	
3¼"	1964-1987	£40-£60	$85-$125	_____	_____	☐

Boswell Designed by Jean Walmsley Heap

Size	Production dates	Market value		Date acquired	Price paid	
3½"	1972-Cur	RRP	RRP	_____	_____	☐

RRP = Recommended Retail Price

Butterfingers Designed by Doreen Noel Roberts

Size	Production dates	Market value	Date acquired	Price paid	
3¼"	1991-Cur	RRP	RRP	_____	_____	☐

Casanova Designed by Jean Walmsley Heap

Size	Production dates	Market value	Date acquired	Price paid	
3¼"	1982-Cur	RRP	RRP	_____	_____	☐

Cha Cha Designed by Jean Walmsley Heap

Size	Production dates	Market value	Date acquired	Price paid	
5"	1959-1961	£1000-£1500 $2150-$3000	_____	_____	☐

Charlotte Designed by Doreen Noel Roberts

Size	Production dates	Market value	Date acquired	Price paid	
3¾"	1990-1992	£50-£80	$100-$165	_____	_____	☐

Chirpy Designed by Doreen Noel Roberts

Size	Production dates	Market value	Date acquired	Price paid	
3½"	1989-1992	£40-£60	$85-$125	_____	_____	☐

Clanger Designed by Jean Walmsley Heap

Size	Production dates	Market value	Date acquired	Price paid	
3½"	1983-Cur	RRP	RRP	_____	_____	☐

Cookie Designed by Doreen Noel Roberts

Size	Production dates	Market value	Date acquired	Price paid	
4¼"	1995-Cur	RRP	RRP	_____	_____	☐

Cheeky Designed by Doreen Noel Roberts

Size	Production dates	Market value	Date acquired	Price paid	
3½"	1996-Cur	RRP	RRP	_____	_____	☐

Cousin Beau Designed by Doreen Noel Roberts

Size	Production dates	Market value	Date acquired	Price paid	
3¾"	1993-Cur	RRP	RRP	_____	_____	☐

Crocker Designed by Doreen Noel Roberts

Size	Production dates	Market value	Date acquired	Price paid	
5"	1980-1989	£30-£40	$60-$85	_____	_____	☐

Dandy Designed by Doreen Noel Roberts

Size	Production dates	Market value	Date acquired	Price paid	
4¼"	1981-Cur	RRP	RRP	_____	_____	☐

Digit Designed by Doreen Noel Roberts

Size	Production dates	Market value		Date acquired	Price paid	
$3\frac{1}{4}''$	1991-Cur	RRP	RRP	_____	_____	☐

Dobbin Designed by Jean Walmsley Heap

Size	Production dates	Market value		Date acquired	Price paid	
$3\frac{3}{4}''$	1995-Cur	RRP	RRP	_____	_____	☐

Dodger Designed by Jean Walmsley Heap

Size	Production dates	Market value		Date acquired	Price paid	
4″	1964-1995	£30-£50	$60-$95	_____	_____	☐

Duffy Designed by Jean Walmsley Heap

Size	Production dates	Market value		Date acquired	Price paid	
4″	1989-Cur	RRP	RRP	_____	_____	☐

Euclid Designed by Jean Walmsley Heap

Size	Production dates	Market value		Date acquired	Price paid	
3″	1989-Cur	RRP	RRP	_____	_____	☐

Father Designed by Jean Walmsley Heap
Dungarees

Size	Production dates	Market value		Date acquired	Price paid	
8″	1955-1960	£700-£1000	$1450-$2000	_____	_____	☐

Kipper Tie

Size	Production dates	Market value		Date acquired	Price paid	
8″	1960-1970	£400-£600	$800-$1200	_____	_____	☐

Father Designed by Jean Walmsley Heap

Size	Production dates	Market value		Date acquired	Price paid	
8″	1977-Cur	RRP	RRP	_____	_____	☐

Forty Winks Designed by Doreen Noel Roberts

Size	Production dates	Market value		Date acquired	Price paid	
$4\frac{1}{2}''$ L	1993-1995	£30-£50	$60-$95	_____	_____	☐

Gussie Designed by Jean Walmsley Heap

Size	Production dates	Market value		Date acquired	Price paid	
3″	1960-1968	£300-£400	$600-$800	_____	_____	☐

Honey Designed by Doreen Noel Roberts

Size	Production dates	Market value		Date acquired	Price paid	
$3\frac{1}{2}''$	1989-1992	£30-£50	$60-$100	_____	_____	☐

Humphrey Go-Kart Designed by Jean Walmsley Heap

Size	Production dates	Market value		Date acquired	Price paid	
4½"	1988-1994	£40-£60	$80-$120			☐

Jacky Designed by Doreen Noel Roberts

Size	Production dates	Market value		Date acquired	Price paid	
3¾"	1992-Cur	RRP	RRP			☐

Jim Lad Designed by Doreen Noel Roberts

Size	Production dates	Market value		Date acquired	Price paid	
5"	1986-1992	£60-£100	$120-$205			☐

Jingle Designed by Doreen Noel Roberts

Size	Production dates	Market value		Date acquired	Price paid	
3¼"	1985-1992	£40-£60	$80-$125			☐

Little Mo Designed by Doreen Noel Roberts

Size	Production dates	Market value		Date acquired	Price paid	
2"	1986-1994	£30-£40	$60-$85			☐

Lucy Pocket Designed by Jean Walmsley Heap

Size	Production dates	Market value		Date acquired	Price paid	
4"	1960-1967	£80-£120	$160-$250			☐

Margot Designed by Jean Walmsley Heap
Pleated

Size	Production dates	Market value		Date acquired	Price paid	
3½"	1956-1957	£150-£250	$300-$500			☐

Straight

Size	Production dates	Market value		Date acquired	Price paid	
3½"	1957-1967	£80-£120	$160-$250			☐

Maud Designed by Jean Walmsley Heap

Size	Production dates	Market value		Date acquired	Price paid	
3¼"	1967-1978	£100-£200	$200-$400			☐

Megan The Harp Designed by Jean Walmsley Heap

Size	Production dates	Market value		Date acquired	Price paid	
4"	1960-1967	£200-£400	$400-$800			☐

RRP = Recommended Retail Price

Midge Designed by Jean Walmsley Heap
3 Crumbs

Size	Production dates	Market value	Date acquired	Price paid	
3″	1956-1965 £150-£250	$300-$500			☐

2 Crumbs

Size	Production dates	Market value	Date acquired	Price paid	
3"	1956-1965 £100-£200	$200-$400			☐

Picnic

Size	Production dates	Market value	Date acquired	Price paid	
3½″	1965-Cur RRP	RRP			☐

Mike Designed by Doreen Noel Roberts

Size	Production dates	Market value	Date acquired	Price paid	
4¾″	1994-Cur RRP	RRP			☐

Moppet Designed by Jean Walmsley Heap

Size	Production dates	Market value	Date acquired	Price paid	
4″	1996-Cur RRP	RRP			☐

Mother Designed by Jean Walmsley Heap

Size	Production dates	Market value	Date acquired	Price paid	
8″	1956-1978 £200-£400	$400-$800			☐
8″	1977-Cur RRP	RRP			☐

Fringing To Shawl

Size	Production dates	Market value	Date acquired	Price paid	
8″	1956-1978 £250-£350	$500-$700			☐

Thin Neck

Size	Production dates	Market value	Date acquired	Price paid	
8″	1956-1956 £250-£350	$500-$700			☐

Muncher Designed by Doreen Noel Roberts

Size	Production dates	Market value	Date acquired	Price paid	
5″	1965-1983 £60-£100	$120-$200			☐

New Boy Designed by Doreen Noel Roberts

Size	Production dates	Market value	Date acquired	Price paid	
3½″	1990-Cur RRP	RRP			☐

Nipper Designed by Doreen Noel Roberts

Size	Production dates	Market value	Date acquired	Price paid	
4″	1981-1989 £60-£100	$120-$200			☐

RRP = Recommended Retail Price

Oliver Designed by Doreen Noel Roberts

Size	Production dates	Market value		Date acquired	Price paid	
3¾"	1984-1995	£40-£60	$80-$120			☐

Parsley Designed by Doreen Noel Roberts

Size	Production dates	Market value		Date acquired	Price paid	
3¾"	1987-Cur	RRP	RRP			☐

Peeps Designed by Jean Walmsley Heap

Size	Production dates	Market value		Date acquired	Price paid	
3½"L	1966-Cur	RRP	RRP			☐

Pepper Designed by Doreen Noel Roberts

Size	Production dates	Market value		Date acquired	Price paid	
3¼"	1995-Cur	RRP	RRP			☐

Phumph Designed by Doreen Noel Roberts

Size	Production dates	Market value		Date acquired	Price paid	
4"	1967-1985	£50-£80	$100-$160			☐

Picnic Basket Designed by Jean Walmsley Heap

Size	Production dates	Market value		Date acquired	Price paid	
2"	1966-1968	£300-£500	$600-$1000			☐

Pie Face Designed by Doreen Noel Roberts

Size	Production dates	Market value		Date acquired	Price paid	
4"	1966-1987	£100-£200	£200-$400			☐

Pipkin Designed by Jean Walmsley Heap

Size	Production dates	Market value		Date acquired	Price paid	
3½"	1994-Cur	RRP	RRP			☐

Poppet Designed by Doreen Noel Roberts
2 or 3 Weaves

Size	Production dates	Market value		Date acquired	Price paid	
3½"	1964-Cur	RRP	RRP			☐

Rambler Designed by Doreen Noel Roberts
Red, Green or Yellow

Size	Production dates	Market value		Date acquired	Price paid	
4"	1991-Cur	RRP	RRP			☐

Robert Designed by Jean Walmsley Heap
Satchel

Size	Production dates	Market value		Date acquired	Price paid	
5"	1956-1967	£180-£240	$375-$500			☐

Lollipop

Size	Production dates	Market value		Date acquired	Price paid	
5"	1967-1979	£100-£200	$200-$400			☐

Rocky Designed by Jean Walmsley Heap
1st version

Size	Production dates	Market value		Date acquired	Price paid	
5"	1959-1978	£30-£50	$60-$100			☐

Shoes & Hat

Production dates	Market value	Date acquired	Price paid	
4"	1978-Cur	RRP	RRP	☐

Rolly Designed by Jean Walmsley Heap

Size	Production dates	Market value	Date acquired	Price paid	
4"	1959-Cur	RRP	RRP		☐

Rosa Designed by Jean Walmsley Heap

Size	Production dates	Market value	Date acquired	Price paid	
4"	1982-Cur	RRP	RRP		☐

Blue

Size	Production dates	Market value		Date acquired	Price paid	
4"	1982-1984	£30-£50	$60-$100			☐

Scoffer Designed by Doreen Noel Roberts

Size	Production dates	Market value	Date acquired	Price paid	
3¾"	1991-Cur	RRP	RRP		☐

Scout Designed by Doreen Noel Roberts

Size	Production dates	Market value	Date acquired	Price paid	
5" L	1992-Cur	RRP	RRP		☐

Scrumpy Designed by Jean Walmsley Heap

Size	Production dates	Market value	Date acquired	Price paid	
4"	1985-Cur	RRP	RRP		☐

Shiner Designed by Jean Walmsley Heap

Size	Production dates	Market value		Date acquired	Price paid	
4"	1960-1967	£300-£400	£625-$850			☐

Snuggles Designed by Jean Walmsley Heap

Size	Production dates		Market value		Date acquired	Price paid	
3½"L	1958-Cur	RRP	RRP		_____	_____	☐

Snuggles (Awake) Designed by Jean Walmsley Heap

Size	Production dates		Market value		Date acquired	Price paid	
3½"L	1991-Cur	RRP	RRP		_____	_____	☐

Solo Designed by Doreen Noel Roberts

Size	Production dates	Market value	Date acquired	Price paid	
4¼"	1985-1993	£40-£60	$80-$125	_____	☐

Squeezy Designed by Jean Walmsley Heap

Size	Production dates	Market value	Date acquired	Price paid	
3¼"	1960-1970	£250-£350	$495-$695	_____	☐

Sunny Designed by Doreen Noel Roberts

Size	Production dates		Market value		Date acquired	Price paid	
3¾"	1992-Cur	RRP	RRP		_____	_____	☐

Teddy Designed by Doreen Noel Roberts

Size	Production dates		Market value		Date acquired	Price paid	
3½"	1995-Cur	RRP	RRP		_____	_____	☐

Tennyson Designed by Doreen Noel Roberts

Size	Production dates	Market value	Date acquired	Price paid	
3¾"	1987-1994	£40-£60	$80-$120	_____	☐

Thumper Designed by Jean Walmsley Heap

Size	Production dates		Market value		Date acquired	Price paid	
4"	1967-Cur	RRP	RRP		_____	_____	☐

Tiddler Designed by Doreen Noel Roberts

Size	Production dates		Market value		Date acquired	Price paid	
3¾"	1996-Cur	RRP	RRP		_____	_____	☐

Tippit Designed by Jean Walmsley Heap

Size	Production dates		Market value		Date acquired	Price paid	
3"	1995-Cur	RRP	RRP		_____	_____	☐

Totty Designed by Jean Walmsley Heap

Size	Production dates	Market value	Date acquired	Price paid	
3½"	1971-1981	£50-£80	$100-$160	_____	☐

RRP = Recommended Retail Price

Twins Designed by Jean Walmsley Heap

Size	Production dates		Market value	Date acquired	Price paid	
4"L	1962-Cur	RRP	RRP	_____	_____	☐

Uncle Soames Designed by Jean Walmsley Heap

Size	Production dates		Market value	Date acquired	Price paid	
7½"	1959-1985	£150-£250	$300-$500	_____	_____	☐

Brown Trousers

Size	Production dates		Market value	Date acquired	Price paid	
7½"	1959-1985	£250-£300	$500-$600	_____	_____	☐

Vanilla Designed by Doreen Noel Roberts

Size	Production dates		Market value	Date acquired	Price paid	
3"	1993-Cur	RRP	RRP	_____	_____	☐

Victoria Designed by Jean Walmsley Heap
(Introduced to celebrate the recovery of the fire)

Size	Production dates		Market value	Date acquired	Price paid	
3¼"	1986-Cur	RRP	RRP	_____	_____	☐

Wakey Designed by Jean Walmsley Heap

Size	Production dates		Market value	Date acquired	Price paid	
3½" long	1958-Cur	RRP	RRP	_____	_____	☐

Whopper Designed by Doreen Noel Roberts

Size	Production dates		Market value	Date acquired	Price paid	
4½"	1979-Cur	RRP	RRP	_____	_____	☐

With Silver Brim

Size	Production dates		Market value	Date acquired	Price paid	
		£50-£80	$100-$160	_____	_____	☐

Wordsworth Designed by Doreen Noel Roberts

Size	Production dates		Market value	Date acquired	Price paid	
3½"	1991-1993	£60-£100	$120-$200	_____	_____	☐

RRP = Recommended Retail Price

Members Gifts & Models of the Year

Herald Designed by Jean Walmsley Heap
Founder Member

Size	Production dates	Market value		Date acquired	Price paid	
3½"	Oct.1992- Dec.1993	£70-£100	$140-$200			☐

Bosun Designed by Doreen Noel Roberts
Model of the Year

Size	Production dates		Market value	Date acquired	Price paid	
4½"	1992-1993	£60-£100	$120-$200			☐

Buttons Designed by Doreen Noel Roberts
Membership Gift

Size	Production dates		Market value	Date acquired	Price paid	
4"	Jan.-Dec. 1994	£50-£80	$100-$160			☐

Puffer Designed by Jean Walmsley Heap
Model of the Year

Size	Production dates		Market value	Date acquired	Price paid	
4½"	1994-1994	£50-£80	$100-$160			☐

Bellman Designed by Jean Walmsley Heap
Membership Gift

Size	Production dates		Market value	Date acquired	Price paid	
4½"	Jan.1995- Dec.1996	£50-£80	$100-$160			☐

Georgie & Dragon Designed by Doreen Noel Roberts
Model of the Year

Size	Production dates		Market value	Date acquired	Price paid	
6"	Jan.1995- Mar.1996	£50-£80	$100-$160			☐

Newsie Designed by Doreen Noel Roberts
Membership Gift

Size	Production dates		Market value	Date acquired	Price paid	
4¼"	Jan.-Dec 1996	£30-£50	$60-$100			☐

Delia Designed by Jean Walmsley Heap
Model of the Year

Size	Production dates	Market value		Date acquired	Price paid	
4"	Jan.1996- Mar.1997	RRP	RRP			☐

Event Pieces

Walmsley Designed by Jean Walmsley Heap

Size	Production dates	Market value		Date acquired	Price paid	
4½"W	1994-1994	£80-£120	$160-$250	_____	_____	☐

Runaway Designed by Doreen Noel Roberts

Size	Production dates	Market value		Date acquired	Price paid	
4¾"W	1995-1995	£60-£100	$120-$200	_____	_____	☐

Event Piece Designed by Jean Walmsley Heap
(This piece won't be named until 1997)

Size	Production dates	Market value		Date acquired	Price paid	
?	1996-1996	RRP	RRP	_____	_____	☐

Collectors Plates

Father
Limited Edition of 10000

Size	Production dates	Market value		Date acquired	Price paid	
9" Dia	1982-1984	£60-£100	$120-$200	_____	_____	☐

Mother & Baby
Limited Edition of 10000

Size	Production dates	Market value		Date acquired	Price paid	
9" Dia	1982-1983	£70-£100	$140-$200	_____	_____	☐

Whopper
Limited Edtion of 7500

Size	Production dates	Market value		Date acquired	Price paid	
9" Dia	1982-1985	£60-£100	$120-$200	_____	_____	☐

Gingerbread Day
Limited Edition of 7500

Size	Production dates	Market value		Date acquired	Price paid	
9" Dia	1989-Cur	RRP	RRP	_____	_____	☐

Caravan
Limited Edition of 7500

Size	Production dates	Market value		Date acquired	Price paid	
9" Dia	1990-Cur	RRP	RRP	_____	_____	☐

The Old Schoolhouse
Limited Edition of 7500

Size	Production dates		Market value	Date acquired	Price paid	
9″ Dia	1992-Cur	RRP	RRP	_____	_____	☐

China Wares

Breakfast Sets
(Pink or Blue)

Size	Production dates		Market value	Date acquired	Price paid	
	1992-Cur	RRP	RRP	_____	_____	☐

Mugs
(Pink or Blue)

Size	Production dates		Market value	Date acquired	Price paid	
	1992-Cur	RRP	RRP	_____	_____	☐

Tea For Two Set

Size	Production dates		Market value	Date acquired	Price paid	
	1992-Cur	RRP	RRP	_____	_____	☐

Trinket Boxes
Sml, Med, Lg

Size	Production dates		Market value	Date acquired	Price paid	
	1992-Cur	RRP	RRP	_____	_____	☐

Wall Mounted Pictures

The Dance

Size	Production dates	Market value	Date acquired	Price paid	
14″x20″	1989-1994	£30-£50	$60-$100	_____	☐

The Auction

Size	Production dates	Market value	Date acquired	Price paid	
14″x20″	1989-1994	£30-£50	$60-$100	_____	☐

The Homestead

Size	Production dates	Market value	Date acquired	Price paid	
14″x20″	1989-1994	£30-£50	$60-$100	_____	☐

RRP = Recommended Retail Price

Buildings and Accessories

Apple Barrel Designed by Doreen Noel Roberts

Size	Production dates	Market value	Date acquired	Price paid	
2"Dia	1985-1992	£20-£30	$40-$60		☐

Balcony Scene Designed by Doreen Noel Roberts

Size	Production dates	Market value	Date acquired	Price paid	
8½"L	1992-Cur	RRP	RRP		☐

Bandstand Designed by Jean Walmsley Heap

Size	Production dates	Market value	Date acquired	Price paid	
12"	1964-1973	£250-£350	$525-$750		☐

Remodelled

Size	Production dates	Market value	Date acquired	Price paid	
12"	1973-Cur	RRP	RRP		☐

Bath Tub Designed by Doreen Noel Roberts

Size	Production dates	Market value	Date acquired	Price paid	
3"L	1967-1975	£40-£60	$80-$125		☐

Remodelled

Size	Production dates	Market value	Date acquired	Price paid	
3"L	1982	£20-£30	$40-$60		☐

Cake Stand Designed by Jean Walmsley Heap

Size	Production dates	Market value	Date acquired	Price paid	
5" L	1966-1972	£250-£300	$495-$595		☐

Camp Fire Designed by Doreen Noel Roberts

The Camp Fire model came with smoke initially, however due to possible danger to children it stopped being produced, The Camp Fire is now sold without smoke.

Size	Production dates	Market value	Date acquired	Price paid	
4½"W	1993-Cur	RRP	RRP		☐

The Caravan Designed by Doreen Noel Roberts

Size	Production dates	Market value	Date acquired	Price paid	
8½"	1976-Cur	RRP	RRP		☐

Castle Tavern Designed by Doreen Noel Roberts

Size	Production dates	Market value	Date acquired	Price paid	
11"	1968-Cur	RRP	RRP		☐

RRP = Recommended Retail Price

Christmas Cabin Designed by Jean Walmsley Heap

Size	Production dates	Market value		Date acquired	Price paid	
6"	1996-Cur	RRP	RRP	_____	_____	☐

Christmas Island Designed by Jean Walmsley Heap
With Foilage

Size	Production dates	Market value		Date acquired	Price paid	
15"	1996-Cur	RRP	RRP	_____	_____	☐

Christmas Scene Designed by Doreen Noel Roberts
Limited Edition of 2000

Size	Production dates	Market value		Date acquired	Price paid	
10¼"	1985-1986	£500-£1000	$1150-$2225	_____	_____	☐

Cobble Cottage Designed by Doreen Noel Roberts

Size	Production dates	Market value		Date acquired	Price paid	
8"	1967-Cur	RRP	RRP	_____	_____	☐

Curiosity Shop Designed by Doreen Noel Roberts

Size	Production dates	Market value		Date acquired	Price paid	
12"	1976-Cur	RRP	RRP	_____	_____	☐

Easel Wedge Designed by Jean Walmsley Heap

Size	Production dates	Market value		Date acquired	Price paid	
3"L	1968-1971	£60-£100	$125-$200	_____	_____	☐

Fruit Shop Designed by Jean Walmsley Heap

Size	Production dates	Market value		Date acquired	Price paid	
11"L	1968-Cur	RRP	RRP	_____	_____	☐

Grandstand Designed by Jean Walmsley Heap

Size	Production dates	Market value		Date acquired	Price paid	
14½"L	1961-1969	£100-£200	$125-$200	_____	_____	☐

Remodelled

Size	Production dates	Market value		Date acquired	Price paid	
14½"L	1990-1995	£80-£120	$160-$245	_____	_____	☐

The Jetty Designed by Jean Walmsley Heap

Size	Production dates	Market value		Date acquired	Price paid	
14"Dia	1979-Cur	RRP	RRP	_____	_____	☐

The Kitchen Designed by Jean Walmsley Heap

Size	Production dates	Market value		Date acquired	Price paid	
8"	1995-Cur	RRP	RRP	_____	_____	☐

Grandstand (1st version).   *Milk Jug Stand.*

Large House Designed by Jean Walmsley Heap

Size	Production dates		Market value	Date acquired	Price paid	
19″	1966-Cur	RRP	RRP	_____	_____	☐

Model Stand Designed by Jean Walmsley Heap
Rabbit

Size	Production dates	Market value		Date acquired	Price paid	
9½″ L	1960-1967	£200-£400	£425-$850	_____	_____	☐

Pendelfin

Size	Production dates	Market value		Date acquired	Price paid	
9½″ L	1960-1967	£150-£250	$300-$495	_____	_____	☐

Milk Jug Stand Designed by Jean Walmsley Heap

Size	Production dates	Market value		Date acquired	Price paid	
5″ L	1966-1972	£300-£500	$600-$1100	_____	_____	☐

Old School House Designed by Jean Walmsley Heap

Size	Production dates		Market value	Date acquired	Price paid	
13½″ W	1989-Cur	RRP	RRP	_____	_____	☐

Piano & Plant Designed by Jean Walmsley Heap

Size	Production dates		Market value	Date acquired	Price paid	
3″	1965-Cur	RRP	RRP	_____	_____	☐

Picnic Island Designed by Jean Walmsley Heap

Size	Production dates		Market value	Date acquired	Price paid	
11″ L	1985-Cur	RRP	RRP	_____	_____	☐

Picnic Stand Designed by Jean Walmsley Heap

Size	Production dates	Market value		Date acquired	Price paid	
9″ L	1965-1985	£80-£120	$160-$245	_____	_____	☐

Raft Designed by Jean Walmsley Heap

Size	Production dates	Market value		Date acquired	Price paid	
7"L	1983-Cur	RRP	RRP	_____	_____	☐

Robins Cave Designed by Doreen Noel Roberts

Size	Production dates	Market value		Date acquired	Price paid	
7½"L	1995-Cur	RRP	RRP	_____	_____	☐

Shrimp Stand Designed by Doreen Noel Roberts

Size	Production dates	Market value		Date acquired	Price paid	
10"L	1966-1982	£60-£100	$125-$200	_____	_____	☐

Timber Stand Designed by Doreen Noel Roberts

Size	Production dates	Market value		Date acquired	Price paid	
10"L	1966-1982	£40-£60	$80-$120	_____	_____	☐

The Toyshop Designed by Doreen Noel Roberts

Size	Production dates	Market value		Date acquired	Price paid	
10½"W	1992-Cur	RRP	RRP	_____	_____	☐

Wishing Well Designed by Jean Walmsley Heap

Size	Production dates	Market value		Date acquired	Price paid	
8"L	1994-Cur	RRP	RRP	_____	_____	☐

Wall Plaques & Ornamental Ware

Balcony Scene Designed by Doreen Noel Roberts

Size	Production dates	Market value		Date acquired	Price paid	
8½x8½"	1982-Cur	RRP	RRP	_____	_____	☐

Balloon Woman Wall Figure Designed by Jean Walmsley Heap

Size	Production dates	Market value		Date acquired	Price paid	
3"	1955-1956	£400-£600	$800-$1200	_____	_____	☐

Bellman Wall Figure Designed by Jean Walmsley Heap

Size	Production dates	Market value		Date acquired	Price paid	
3"	1955-1956	£400-£600	$800-$1200	_____	_____	☐

Bobbin Woman Figure Designed by Jean Walmsley Heap
Only 2 made

Size	Production dates	Market value		Date acquired	Price paid	
5"	1955-1959	£2000-£3000	$5000-$7500	_____	_____	☐

RRP = Recommended Retail Price

The Bellman plaque   Balloon Woman plaque

Cauldron Witch Figure Designed by Jean Walmsley Heap

Size	Production dates	Market value	Date acquired	Price paid	
Size	*Production dates*	*Market value*	*Date acquired*	*Price paid*	
4½"	1953-1959	£600-£800	$1250-$1650		☐

Cornish Prayer Figure Designed by Jean Walmsley Heap

Size	Production dates	Market value	Date acquired	Price paid	
Size	*Production dates*	*Market value*	*Date acquired*	*Price paid*	
4"	1962-1965	£400-£600	$825-$1200		☐

Cyril Squirrel Designed by Doreen Noel Roberts

Size	Production dates	Market value	Date acquired	Price paid	
Size	*Production dates*	*Market value*	*Date acquired*	*Price paid*	
6½"	1963-1965	£1000-£2000	$2225-$4500		☐

Daisy Duck Designed by Jean Walmsley Heap

Size	Production dates	Market value	Date acquired	Price paid	
Size	*Production dates*	*Market value*	*Date acquired*	*Price paid*	
4½"	1955-1958	£800-£1200	$1650-$2500		☐

Desmond Duck Designed by Jean Walmsley Heap

Size	Production dates	Market value	Date acquired	Price paid	
Size	*Production dates*	*Market value*	*Date acquired*	*Price paid*	
4½"	1955-1958	£800-£1200	$1650-$2500		☐

Elf Wall Figure Designed by Jean Walmsley Heap

Size	Production dates	Market value	Date acquired	Price paid	
Size	*Production dates*	*Market value*	*Date acquired*	*Price paid*	
3"	1955-1956	£400-£600	$825-$1200		☐

Fairy Jardiniere with Bookends
Designed by Jean Walmsley Heap

Size	Production dates	Market value	Date acquired	Price paid	
Size	*Production dates*	*Market value*	*Date acquired*	*Price paid*	
5¼"	1954-1958	£2500-£3500	$5500-$7250		☐

RRP = Recommended Retail Price

Flying Witch plaque   *Daisy Duck.*

Fairy Shop Plaque Designed by Jean Walmsley Heap
Coloured

Size	Production dates	Market value	Date acquired	Price paid	
16 x 10½"	1954-1958	£1500-£2500 $3000-$5000			☐

Brown Glaze

Size	Production dates	Market value	Date acquired	Price paid	
16 x 10½"	1954-1958	£800-£1200 $1625-$2500			☐

Remodelled and signed

Size	Production dates	Market value	Date acquired	Price paid	
16 x 10½"	1992-1992	£1000-£2000 $2250-$4500			☐

Flying Witch Wall Figure Designed by Jean Walmsley Heap

Size	Production dates	Market value	Date acquired	Price paid	
3"	1955-1956	£400-£600 $825-$1250			☐

Gallery Series Plaques
Pieface, Poppet, Wakey Designed by Doreen Noel Roberts
Dodger, Robert, Gallery Designed by Jean Walmsley Heap

Size	Production dates	Market value	Date acquired	Price paid	
3x4"	1968-1971	£300-£500 $600-$1000 each			☐

Herald Wall Figure Designed by Jean Walmsley Heap

Size	Production dates	Market value	Date acquired	Price paid	
3"	1955-1956	£400-£600 $800-$1225			☐

Manx Kitten Designed by Jean Walmsley Heap

Size	Production dates	Market value	Date acquired	Price paid	
3½"	1956-1958	£1800-£2500 $4000-$5500			☐

Mouse House Match Holder Designed by Doreen Noel Roberts

Size	Production dates	Market value	Date acquired	Price paid	
3"	1964-1969	£300-£500 $600-$1000			☐

Old Adam Figure Designed by Jean Walmsley Heap

Size	Production dates	Market value	Date acquired	Price paid	
8"	1955-1956	£1000-£1500 $2200-$3500			☐

Old Meg Plaque Designed by Jean Walmsley Heap

Size	Production dates	Market value	Date acquired	Price paid	
5"	1953-1954	£2000-£3000 $4500-6500			☐

Pendle Witch Plaque Designed by Jean Walmsley Heap

Size	Production dates	Market value	Date acquired	Price paid	
8"	1953-1957	£1500-£2000 $3250-$4500			☐

Phynnodderee (Manx Pixie) Designed by Jean Walmsley Heap

Size	Production dates	Market value	Date acquired	Price paid	
3"	1955-1956	£1500-£2000 $3250-$4500			☐

Pixie Bods Designed by Jean Walmsley Heap

Size	Production dates	Market value	Date acquired	Price paid	
4"	1965-1967	£300-£500 $625-$1000			☐

Pixie Bods Caravan Designed by Jean Walmsley Heap
(approx. 14 issued)

Size	Production dates	Market value	Date acquired	Price paid	
12"	1965-1965	£3000-£5000 $6500-$12000			☐

Pixie House Plaque Designed by Jean Walmsley Heap

Size	Production dates	Market value	Date acquired	Price paid	
8"	1953-1958	£1500-£2000 $3250-$4500			☐

The Pooch Designed by Doreen Noel Roberts

Size	Production dates	Market value	Date acquired	Price paid	
3¾"L	1962-1987	£50-£80 $100-$160			☐

Rabbit Bookends Designed by Jean Walmsley Heap
Coloured

Size	Production dates	Market value	Date acquired	Price paid	
5"	1958-1965	£3000-£5000 $6500-$12000			☐

Rheingold Lamp Designed by Jean Walmsley Heap
Wooden Base

Size	Production dates	Market value	Date acquired	Price paid	
	1954-1956	£1500-£2000 $3250-$4500			☐

Stone Craft Base

Size	Production dates	Market value	Date acquired	Price paid	
	1954-1958	£1000-£2000 $2250-$4500			☐

Romeo and Juliet plaque. *The Toper plaque*

Romeo & Juliet Wall Figures
Designed by Jean Walmsley Heap

Size	Production dates	Market value		Date acquired	Price paid	
8"	1957-1959	£1500-£2500	$3250-$5500			☐

Scrooge Wall Figure Designed by Jean Walmsley Heap

Size	Production dates	Market value		Date acquired	Price paid	
3"	1955-1956	£400-£600	$805-$1225			☐

Shaggy Dog Wall Plaque Designed by Jean Walmsley Heap

Size	Production dates	Market value		Date acquired	Price paid	
5"	1955-1958	£500-£800	$1000-$1625			☐

Tammy Puppy Designed by Jean Walmsley Heap

Size	Production dates	Market value		Date acquired	Price paid	
3"	1957-1987	£50-£80	$100-$165			☐

Tipsy Witch Designed by Jean Walmsley Heap

Size	Production dates	Market value		Date acquired	Price paid	
4½"	1953-1959	£300-£500	$625-$1050			☐

Toper Wall Figure Designed by Jean Walmsley Heap

Size	Production dates	Market value		Date acquired	Price paid	
3"	1955-1956	£400-£600	$825-$1250			☐

Deep Relief Nursery Rhyme Characters
Tom the Pipers Son Designed by Jean Walmsley Heap

Size	Production dates	Market value		Date acquired	Price paid	
5"	1956-1959	£300-£500	$625-$1100			☐

Little Bo Peep Designed by Jean Walmsley Heap

Size	Production dates	Market value		Date acquired	Price paid	
5"	1956-1959	£300-£500	$625-$1100			☐

Wee Willie Winkie Designed by Jean Walmsley Heap

Size	Production dates	Market value		Date acquired	Price paid	
5"	1956-1959	£300-£500	$625-$1050	_____	_____	☐

Little Jack Horner Designed by Jean Walmsley Heap

Size	Production dates	Market value		Date acquired	Price paid	
5"	1956-1959	£300-£500	$625-$1050	_____	_____	☐

Mary Mary Designed by Jean Walmsley Heap

Size	Production dates	Market value		Date acquired	Price paid	
5"	1956-1959	£300-£500	$625-$1050	_____	_____	☐

Miss Muffet Designed by Jean Walmsley Heap

Size	Production dates	Market value		Date acquired	Price paid	
5"	1956-1959	£300-£500	$625-$1050	_____	_____	☐

Set of Six		£2500-£3500	$5500-$7500	_____	_____	☐

Pendelfin Mouse Family

The first models of the mice where produced with a grey glaze. Because they stood out from the rabbits the glaze was changed to brown and the mouse family then blended in more with the rabbit collections.

Mother Mouse Designed by Jean Walmsley Heap

Grey

Size	Production dates	Market value		Date acquired	Price paid	
4½"	1961-1966	£500-£800	$1100-$1650	_____	_____	☐

Brown

Size	Production dates	Market value		Date acquired	Price paid	
4½"	1961-1966	£300-£500	$600-$1000	_____	_____	☐

Father Mouse Designed by Jean Walmsley Heap
Grey

Size	Production dates	Market value		Date acquired	Price paid	
4½"	1961-1966	£500-£800	$1100-$1650			☐

Brown

Size	Production dates	Market value		Date acquired	Price paid	
4½"	1961-1966	£300-£500	$600-$1000			☐

Lollipop Mouse Designed by Jean Walmsley Heap
Grey

Size	Production dates	Market value		Date acquired	Price paid	
4½"	1961-1966	£600-£800	$1250-$1625			☐

Brown

Size	Production dates	Market value		Date acquired	Price paid	
4½"	1961-1966	£400-£600	$810-$1225			☐

PenDelfin Charms

Totty

Size	Production dates	Market value		Date acquired	Price paid	
10mm	1979-1980	£80-£120	$160-$250			☐

Muncher

Size	Production dates	Market value		Date acquired	Price paid	
10mm	1979-1980	£80-£120	$160-$250			☐

Phumf

Size	Production dates	Market value		Date acquired	Price paid	
10mm	1979-1980	£80-£120	$160-$250			☐

Barney

Size	Production dates	Market value		Date acquired	Price paid	
10mm	1979-1980	£80-£120	$160-$250			☐
Solid gold limited edition of six						
		£250-£350	£550-$775			☐

Midge

Size	Production dates	Market value		Date acquired	Price paid	
10mm	1979-1980	£80-£120	$160-$250			☐

RRP = Recommended Retail Price

Wakey

Size	Production dates	Market value		Date acquired	Price paid	
10mm	1979-1980	£80-£120	$160-$250	_____	_____	☐

Full set of six		£700-£1000	$1500-$2250	_____	_____	☐

The Metallion Range

Bronze Plant Pot Designed by Doreen Noel Roberts

Size	Production dates	Market value		Date acquired	Price paid	
	1980-1985	£250-£350	$525-$750	_____	_____	☐

Bronze Column Designed by Doreen Noel Roberts

Size	Production dates	Market value		Date acquired	Price paid	
	1980-1985	£300-£500	$600-$1000	_____	_____	☐

Dove Chalice Designed by Doreen Noel Roberts

Size	Production dates	Market value		Date acquired	Price paid	
13½"	1980-1985	£300-£500	$600-$1000	_____	_____	☐

Dragon Flower Holder Designed by Jean Walmsley Heap

Size	Production dates	Market value		Date acquired	Price paid	
8"	1980-1985	£150-£250	$310-$500	_____	_____	☐

Dragon Candle Holder Designed by Jean Walmsley Heap

Size	Production dates	Market value		Date acquired	Price paid	
5"	1980-1985	£120-£180	$250-$375	_____	_____	☐

Elf Tree Flower Holder Designed by Doreen Noel Roberts

Size	Production dates	Market value		Date acquired	Price paid	
4"	1980-1985	£300-£500	$650-$1100	_____	_____	☐

Elf Tree Candle Holder Designed by Doreen Noel Roberts

Size	Production dates	Market value		Date acquired	Price paid	
4"	1980-1985	£150-£250	$310-$500	_____	_____	☐

Flying Witch Wall Plaque Designed by Jean Walmsley Heap

Size	Production dates	Market value		Date acquired	Price paid	
8"L	1980-1985	£500-£800	$1100-$1650	_____	_____	☐

Ivy Leaf Posy Bowl Designed by Doreen Noel Roberts

Size	Production dates	Market value		Date acquired	Price paid	
6½" Dia	1980-1985	£150-£250	$320-$525	_____	_____	☐

Rabbit Bookends Designed by Jean Walmsley Heap

Size	Production dates	Market value		Date acquired	Price paid	
8¼"	1980-1985	£800-£1200	$1650-$2500	_____	_____	☐

Shell Flower Holder Designed by Jean Walmsley Heap

Size	Production dates	Market value		Date acquired	Price paid	
11½"	1980-1985	£300-£500	$610-$1100	_____	_____	☐
7½"	1980-1985	£180-£240	$375-$500	_____	_____	☐

Sunflower Plinth Designed by Doreen Noel Roberts

Size	Production dates	Market value		Date acquired	Price paid	
	1980-1985	£150-£250	$310-$500	_____	_____	☐

Swan Child Wall Sculpture Designed by Doreen Noel Roberts

Size	Production dates	Market value		Date acquired	Price paid	
12"	1980-1985	£400-£600	$825-$1350	_____	_____	☐

Limited Editions

Rose Dragon (100) Designed by Jean Walmsley Heap

Size	Production dates	Market value		Date acquired	Price paid	
18"		£1500-£2500	$4000-$5500	_____	_____	☐

Leaping Salmon (250)

Designed especially for Pendelfin by Hugh Dereck
The Salmon was also produced in a Pewter Finish.

Size	Production dates	Market value		Date acquired	Price paid	
25"		£1000-£2000	$2500-$5000	_____	_____	☐

Swan Child Wall Sculpture (2) Designed by Doreen Noel Roberts

Ivory Finish

Size	Production dates	Market value		Date acquired	Price paid	
		£450-£550	$900-$1250	_____	_____	☐

RRP = Recommended Retail Price

Recent prices achieved at auction

Mother (Thin Neck)
realised £180.

Uncle Soames
realised £80.

Cha Cha realised
£680.

Aunt Agatha realised £910.

Father (Kipper Tie)
realised £200.

Lollipop Mouse
realised £600.

Megan the Harp realised £210 whilst
Squeezy, realised £160.

Index

Colour pictures are shown in **bold**, black and white pictures in *italic* and entry in price listing in roman

Name of Model	Series	Page no
Angelo	Rabbits	**33**, 78
Apple Barrel	Buildings and Accessories	90
Auction	Wall Mounted Picture	**59**, 89
Aunt Agatha	Rabbits	**45**, *102*, 78
Aunt Ruby	Rabbits	**30**, **60**, 78
Balcony Scene	Ornamental Ware	**52**, 93
Balcony Scene	Buildings and Accessories	90
Balloon Woman	Wall Plaque	**47**, 93, *94*
Bandstand	Buildings and Accessories	**17**, 90
Barney	PenDelfin Charms	99
Barney	Rabbits	**40**, 78
Barrow Boy	Rabbits	78
Bath Tub	Buildings and Accessories	**40**, 90
Bellman	Membership Gift	**31**, 87
Bellman	Wall Plaque	**47**, 93, *94*
Big Spender	Rabbits	**43**, 78
Birdie	Rabbits	**20**, **44**, 78
Blossom	Rabbits	**38**, **40**, 78
Bobbin Woman	Figure	93
Bobby	Rabbits	78
Bongo	Rabbits	**17**, **34**, 78
Bosun	Model of the Year	**24**, **32**, 78, 87
Boswell	Rabbits	**38**
Breakfast Sets	China Wares	89
Bronze Column	Metallion Range	100
Bronze Plant Pot	Metallion Range	100
Butterfingers	Rabbits	**33**, **39**, 79
Buttons	Membership Gift	**31**, 87
Cake Stand	Buildings and Accessories	**54**, 90
Camp Fire	Buildings and Accessories	**26**, 90
Caravan	Collector Plate	*14*, 88
Caravan	Buildings and Accessories	90
Casanova	Rabbits	79
Castle Tavern	Buildings and Accessories	**27**, 90
Cauldron Witch	Figure	**53**, 94
Cha Cha	Rabbits	**48**, *102*, 79
Charlotte	Rabbits	**39**, 79
Cheeky	Rabbits	**39**, 79
Chirpy	Rabbits	**21**, 79
Christmas Cabin	Buildings and Accessories	91
Christmas Island	Buildings and Accessories	91
Christmas Scene	Buildings and Accessories	**56**, 91
Clanger	Rabbits	**17**, **34**, 79
Cobble Cottage	Buildings and Accessories	**28**, 91
Cookie	Rabbits	**39**, 79
Cornish Prayer	Figure	**52**, 94
Cousin Beau	Rabbits	**30**, 79
Crocker	Rabbits	**22**, **33**, 79

Curiosity Shop	Buildings and Accessories	91
Cyril Squirrel	Figure	**45**, 94
Daisy Duck	Figure	**61**, 94, *95*
Dance	Wall Mounted Picture	**59**, 89
Dandy	Rabbits	**36**, **40**, *79*
Delia	Model of the Year	**32**, **39**, 87
Desmond Duck	Figure	94
Digit	Rabbits	**19**, 80
Dobbin	Rabbits	**20**, 80
Dodger	Rabbits	**21**, 80
Dodger	Gallery Series Plaques	**46**, 95
Dove Chalice	Metallion Range	**64**, 100
Dragon Candle Holder	Metallion	100
Dragon Flower Holder	Metallion Range	*13*, 100
Duffy	Rabbits	**19**, 80
Easel Wedge	Buildings and Accessories	91
Elf	Wall Figure	94
Elf Tree Candle Holder	Metallion Range	100
Elf Tree Flower Holder	Metallion Range	*13*, **63**, 100
Euclid	Rabbits	**19**, 80
Fairy Jardiniere with Bookends		94
Fairy Shop	Plaque	*11*, **57**, 95
Father	Collector Plate	**58**, 88
Father	Rabbits	**30**, **60**, 80
Father (Dungarees)	Rabbits	**45**, *77*, 80
Father (Kipper Tie)	Rabbits	**45**, *102*, 80
Father Mouse	Mouse Family	**53**, 99
Flying Witch	Wall Plaque	**47**, 95, *95*
Flying Witch Wall Plaque	Metallion Range	100
Forty Winks	Rabbits	**18**, **21**, 80
Fruit Shop	Buildings and Accessories	**55**, 91
Georgie & Dragon	Model of the Year	**32**, 87
Gingerbread Day	Collector Plate	*15*, 88
Grandstand	Buildings and Accessories	**51**, 91, *92*
Gussie	Rabbits	80
Herald	Founder Member Gift	**31**, 87
Herald	Wall Figure	95
Homestead	Wall Mounted Picture	**59**, 89
Honey	Rabbits	**19**, **36**, 80
Humphrey Go-Kart	Rabbits	**20**, **44**, 81
Ivy Leaf Posy Bowl	Metallion Range	*14*, 100
Ivy Leaf Candle Holder	Metallion Range	*14*
Jacky	Rabbits	**19**, **33**, 81
Jetty	Buildings and Accessories	**24**, 91
Jim Lad	Rabbits	**24**, 81
Jingle	Rabbits	**17**, **37**, 81
Juliet	Wall Figures	**47**, *97*, *97*
Kitchen	Buildings and Accessories	**39**, 91
Large House	Buildings and Accessories	**29**, 92
Leaping Salmon	Limited Editions	101
Little Bo Peep	Deep Relief Nursery Rhyme Characters	97
Little Jack Horner	Deep Relief Nursery Rhyme Characters	98
Little Mo	Rabbits	**26**, 81
Lollipop Mouse	Mouse Family	**53**, 99, *102*
Lucy Pocket	Rabbits	**48**, 81
Manx Kitten	Wall Plaque	95
Margot (Pleated)	Rabbits	81
Margot (Straight)	Rabbits	**49**, 81

Mary Mary	Deep Relief Nursery Rhyme Characters	98
Maud	Rabbits	**41, 43**, 81
Megan The Harp	Rabbits	**49**, *77, 102*, 81
Midge	PenDelfin Charms	99
Midge (2 Crumbs)	Rabbits	82
Midge (3 Crumbs)	Rabbits	82
Midge (Picnic)	Rabbits	**25**, 82
Mike	Rabbits	**37, 41**, 82
Milk Jug Stand	Buildings and Accessories	**54**, *92*, 92
Miss Muffet	Deep Relief Nursery Rhyme Characters	98
Model Stand (Pendelfin)	Buildings and Accessories	**50**, 92
Model Stand (Rabbit)	Buildings and Accessories	**50**, 92
Moppet	Rabbits	**40**, 82
Mother	Rabbits	**30, 45**, 82
Mother & Baby	Collector Plate	**58**, 88
Mother (Fringing to Shawl)	Rabbits	82
Mother (Thin Neck)	Rabbits	**45**, *77*, 82, *102*
Mother Mouse	Mouse Family	**53**, 98
Mouse House	Match Holder	**51**, 95
Mugs	China Wares	89
Muncher	PenDelfin Charms	*13*, 99
Muncher	Rabbits	**25, 54**, 82
New Boy	Rabbits	**19, 36**, 82
Newsie	Membership Gift	**31**, 87
Nipper	Rabbits	**26, 38**, 82
Old Adam	Figure	96
Old Meg	Plaque	**57**, 96
Old School House	Buildings and Accessories	**19**, 92
Old Schoolhouse	Collector Plate	*15*, 89
Oliver	Rabbits	**39**, 83
Parsley	Rabbits	**18**, 83
Peeps	Rabbits	**18**, 83
Pendle Witch	Plaque	*10*, **55**, 96
Pepper	Rabbits	**39**, 83
Phumf	PenDelfin Charms	*13*, 99
Phumph	Rabbits	**17, 35**, 83
Phynnodderee (Manx Pixie)	Figure	**52**, 96
Piano & Plant	Buildings and Accessories	**17**, 92
Picnic Basket	Rabbits	**25, 63**, 83
Picnic Island	Buildings and Accessories	**25, 51**, 92
Picnic Stand	Buildings and Accessories	**41, 51, 54**, 92
Pie Face	Rabbits	**25**, 83
Pieface	Gallery Series Plaques	**46**, 95
Pipkin	Rabbits	**36, 42**, 83
Pixie Bods	Figure	96
Pixie Bods Caravan	Ornamental Ware	**23**, 96
Pixie House	Plaque	96
Pooch	Figure	**62**, 96
Poppet	Rabbits	**63**, 83
Poppet	Gallery Series Plaques	**46**, 95
Puffer	Model of the Year	**32**, 87
Rabbit	Bookends	**62**, 96
Rabbit Bookends	Metallion Range	**64**, 101
Raft	Buildings and Accessories	**24**, 93
Rambler	Rabbits	**20, 44, 60**, 83
Rheingold	Lamp	96
Robert	Gallery Series Plaques	**46**, 95
Robert (Lollipop)	Rabbits	**25**, 84

Robert (Satchel)	Rabbits	48, 77, 84
Robins Cave	Buildings and Accessories	22, 93
Rocky	Rabbits	17, 34, 77
Rocky (Shoes & Hat)	Rabbits	84
Rolly	Rabbits	35, 84
Romeo	Wall Figures	47, 97, 97
Rosa	Rabbits	35, 41, 77, 84
Rose Dragon	Limited Editions	13, 101
Runaway	Event Piece	42, 88
Scoffer	Rabbits	39, 84
Scout	Rabbits	26, 84
Scrooge	Wall Figure	97
Scrumpy	Rabbits	38, 84
Shaggy Dog	Wall Plaque	57, 97
Shell Flower Holder	Metallion Range	64, 101
Shiner	Rabbits	7, 48, 84
Shrimp Stand	Buildings and Accessories	26, 51, 93
Snuggles	Rabbits	18, 85
Snuggles (Awake)	Rabbits	44, 85
Solo	Rabbits	19, 35, 85
Squeezy	Rabbits	49, 77, 85, 102
Sunflower Plinth	Metallion Range	101
Sunny	Rabbits	43, 85
Swan Child Wall Sculpture	Limited Editions	101
Swan Child Wall Sculpture	Metallion Range	14, 101
Tammy Puppy	Figure	62, 97
Tea For Two Set	China Wares	89
Teddy	Rabbits	18, 85
Tennyson	Rabbits	20, 85
Thumper	Rabbits	34, 85
Tiddler	Rabbits	85
Timber Stand	Buildings and Accessories	51, 93
Tippit	Rabbits	37, 42, 85
Tipsy Witch	Figure	53, 97
Tom the Pipers Son	Deep Relief Nursery Rhyme Characters	97
Toper	Wall Figure	47, 97, 97
Totty	PenDelfin Charms	99
Totty	Rabbits	40, 85
Toyshop	Buildings and Accessories	19, 93
Trinket Boxes	China Wares	89
Twins	Rabbits	18, 86
Uncle Soames	Rabbits	52, 86, 102
Vanilla	Rabbits	43, 86
Victoria	Rabbits	21, 86
Wakey	PenDelfin Charms	100
Wakey	Rabbits	18, 86
Wakey	Gallery Series Plaques	46, 95
Walmsley	Event Piece	42, 88
Wee Willie Winkie	Deep Relief Nursery Rhyme Characters	98
Whopper	Rabbits	86
Whopper	Collector Plate	59, 88
Whopper (With Silver Brim)	Rabbits	24, 86
Wishing Well	Buildings and Accessories	42, 93
Wordsworth	Rabbits	19, 37, 86

Peter Wilson

Francis Joseph
'Collectors Register'

*At Francis Joseph we produce newsletters
containing details and updates of your
particular collectable. Registration is free
and you only have to write or call us
to be placed on our register.*

**If you have purchased this book direct from us –
there is no need to register –
we already have your details and will
keep you up to date.**

*Also, if you have any details which would be helpful
in the next edition of this book, then please write in
with them at the same time*

Telephone: 0181 318 9580

Francis Joseph
15 St Swithuns Road
London SE13 6RW
Telephone: 0181 318 9580
Fax: 0181 318 1987

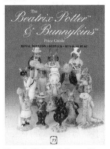

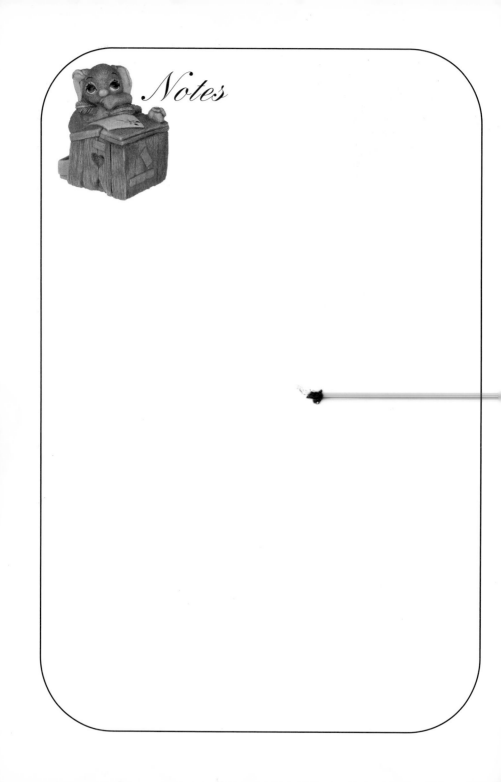

Notes